CONTENTS

KU-646-936

Introduction

Heart Disease is the forty-eighth volume in the **Issues** series. The aim of this series is to offer up-to-date information about important issues in our world.

Heart Disease looks at the causes of heart disease and ways of preventing heart disease.

The information comes from a wide variety of sources and includes:
Government reports and statistics
Newspaper reports and features
Magazine articles and surveys
Literature from lobby groups
and charitable organisations.

It is hoped that, as you read about the many aspects of the issues explored in this book, you will critically evaluate the information presented. It is important that you decide whether you are being presented with facts or opinions. Does the writer give a biased or an unbiased report? If an opinion is being expressed, do you agree with the writer?

Heart Disease offers a useful starting-point for those who need convenient access to information about the many issues involved. However, it is only a starting-point. At the back of the book is a list of organisations which you may want to contact for further information.

*****

Heart disease

Information from Reader's Digest

Coronary death rates have been reduced through improved medical treatment and a better understanding of diet; nevertheless, heart disease still causes one in every four deaths in Britain.

Although coronary heart disease (CHD) is still responsible for more than a quarter of all deaths in Britain, improved treatments have resulted in a dramatic decline in the CHD death rate over the past decade. This fall has been most marked in people below the age of 45.

Nevertheless, Britain still has one of the highest rates of heart disease in the world. More than 300,000 Britons suffer heart attacks each year. A disproportionate number of these people live in Scotland and the north of England where, traditionally, diets are high in saturated fats and low in fresh vegetables. This lends strength to arguments that the antioxidants present in fruit and vegetables may help in the fight against coronary heart disease.

Prevention starts young

Atherosclerosis – or furring up of the arteries – tends to develop over a period of 20 to 30 years, during which there are no symptoms. It is accelerated by smoking.

By the time they reach their 50s, many people have quite badly furred arteries on which plaques (fatty streaks on the walls of the arteries which have developed into fibrous growths) may have already built up, increasing the risk of a heart attack.

The ideal way to prevent atherosclerosis is to take plenty of exercise and to eat a healthy diet that is high in fibre and low in saturated fats (found in high-fat dairy products, fatty meats and hard margarines).

The cholesterol factor

High blood cholesterol levels are accepted as the main underlying cause of coronary heart disease, but such levels are determined by an intricate combination of genetic and dietary factors. In the West, one person in 500 has the misfortune to inherit the predisposition to extremely high blood cholesterol levels; and these people are 20 to 30 times more likely to develop heart disease at an early age than the average person.

Most people, however, bring about their own moderate increase in blood cholesterol levels, by consuming too many saturated fats, or by becoming obese. (Nonetheless, many people who have high blood cholesterol levels are not overweight.) If these factors are combined with smoking, the risk is further increased.

The risk posed by obesity can be reversed by losing weight, because weight loss is usually accompanied by a fall in blood cholesterol levels. This does not include crash dieting, where any loss of weight will be mostly fluid, and regained as soon as you resume a normal diet. The only effective way to lose weight healthily is to cut your intake of fat and refined carbohydrates and to take more exercise. It has also been found that people who maintain their body weight from early adult life, avoiding the fluctuations experienced by many unsuccessful dieters, do not show the same age-related increase in blood cholesterol.

Cholesterol complications

As people grow older their arteries become scarred and partly blocked by atheroma, a fatty substance made of scar tissue and plaques which contains quite large amounts of cholesterol. This condition, called atherosclerosis, progresses more quickly among people with high blood cholesterol levels, particularly if they smoke and have high blood pressure.

If one of the fatty plaques on the wall of a coronary artery ruptures, a blood clot, or thrombosis, forms, blocking the flow of oxygen-laden blood to the heart. The risk of blood clots can be halved through the combination of a careful diet and medication. This means avoiding

heavy, fatty meals, which increase the tendency of the blood to clot, and – in instances where people have already had a heart attack – taking half an aspirin twice weekly.

Who is most at risk?

Among the major factors known to increase the risk of heart disease are raised blood cholesterol levels, cigarette smoking, high blood pressure, obesity and diabetes. In both men and women, the risk of coronary heart disease rises rapidly with increasing age.

Heart disease tends to run in families, so that if either parent, a brother or a sister has suffered a heart attack before the age of 55, the risk to their immediate relatives is ten times greater than for members of families with no history of cardiac problems.

During their reproductive years, while oestrogen keeps their blood cholesterol levels low, women are less prone than men to athero-sclerosis and heart attacks. After the menopause, however, when women's oestrogen levels decline, and their cholesterol levels rise more quickly than those of men, women become increasingly vulnerable to CHD.

Some protection is afforded to women during the menopause and afterwards from hormone replace-ment therapy (HRT), which lowers blood cholesterol levels and thus reduces the risk of a heart attack. Nevertheless, statistically, older women are still more likely to die of heart disease than from any other single cause.

Foods that help

Saturated fatty acids, which are found in hard fats (butter, some margarines, meat and cheese) increase levels of cholesterol in the blood. Replacing these with vegetable oils rich in monounsaturates (such as olive and rapeseed oils) or polyunsaturated fatty acids (such as sunflower, soya and corn oil) reduces cholesterol levels. However, when liquid oils are hardened (by a process called hydrogenation) for commercial use, as in the making of biscuits or margarine, some of them are con-verted into trans fatty acids. Recent research suggests that these 'trans fats' may increase the risk of heart disease as well as raise blood cholesterol levels.

Foods rich in dietary fibre, especially the soluble type found in oats, beans and lentils, can help to lower blood cholesterol levels, though to a lesser extent than is achieved by reducing saturated fat or even dietary cholesterol, such as that found in egg yolks. Including garlic in your diet is said to lower blood cholesterol levels; for many people, garlic pills are a convenient way to boost their intake.

Recent American research seems to show that the more green vegetables you eat, the less likely you are to develop heart problems. Eating moderate amounts of nuts – especi-ally walnuts and almonds – which are rich in polyunsaturated fatty acids, can also reduce coronary risk and can lower blood cholesterol.

Other fatty acids found in oily fish such as herring, mackerel,

pilchards, salmon and sardines are thought to prevent the risk of thrombosis. Eating oily fish twice a week will provide the equivalent of 1 g per day of omega-3, the fatty acid which helps to prevent blood clots forming in arteries. Fish oil supple-ments have the same effect.

A daily dose of alcohol?

Because alcohol dilates small blood vessels and increases the blood flow to the tissues, a moderate intake of up to three glasses of red wine a day can help to stave off coronary heart disease, especially in middle-aged and elderly men, even if they have already had a heart attack. Alcohol also in-creases the level of high density lipo-proteins (HDLs) – protective mole-cules that transport cholesterol away from body tissues and artery walls. But too much alcohol increases blood pressure and can cause irregular heart rhythms, precipitating a coronary attack.

Angina

Common among those in late middle age and the elderly, angina affects 2 million Britons each year. It is caused by the partial obstruction of the coronary arteries so that the heart muscle is not supplied with enough oxygenated blood. With age, these arteries become increasingly thick-ened and less elastic.

Angina is sparked by exertion or stress and is often an indication of a more serious underlying heart condition. It is characterised by discomfort or pain in the chest. This pain may radiate down either arm, across the chest and up to the neck.

Lying down may aggravate it; for the fastest relief, sit or stand quite still. Prompt diagnosis is important: similar pain may also originate from disorders in the upper parts of the digestive tract such as gallstones or stomach ulcers. Smoking, high blood pressure and high blood cholesterol levels accelerate the artery-hardening process.

Angina patients with high blood cholesterol levels should cut down on saturated fats, and may be prescribed cholesterol-lowering drugs.

Fish, fruit and wine

Eating oily fish twice a week may help to prevent heart attacks in people with angina. This is because the fatty acids present in fish oil are thought both to prevent the thickening of arteries and to improve blood flow to the heart.

Some studies suggest that a lack of fruit and vegetables (which provide the antioxidants beta carotene and vitamin C, believed to help protect against hardening of the arteries) predispose people to angina

attacks. It is wise to avoid eating heavy meals which can also lead to an attack.

Boost your intake of anti-oxidants by eating plenty of fruit and vegetables; try drinking a glass or two of red wine. Grape skins, which give red wine its colour, contain powerful antioxidants, and moderate quantities of alcohol may also help by causing tiny blood vessels in the body to dilate.

Britain still tops European heart disease league

By Jeremy Laurance, Health Editor

Government hopes of improving the United Kingdom's dismal standing in the European heart-disease league are doomed, a report shows.

The UK lags so far behind its continental neighbours on heart disease and breast cancer deaths that it is unlikely to catch up. Even if the Government hit its targets for cutting deaths from heart disease, Britain would still be at the back of the field, experts said.

Figures yesterday from the Office of Health Economics (OHE), a think-tank funded by the pharmaceutical industry, show that Britain has among the worst death rates from heart disease and breast cancer in the Western world.

The death rate for heart disease in England and Wales, at 230 per 100,000 population aged 45 to 64, was (around 1995) more than twice that in France and Italy and for breast cancer, at 48 per 100,000, it was one-third higher than in the United States and Canada.

Under the Government's public-health strategy in the White Paper *Saving Lives: our healthier nation*, published last month, targets were set for cutting heart disease by 40 per cent and all cancers by 20 per cent by 2010 in people under 75.

But a 40 per cent cut in the heart-disease rate for England and

Wales would still leave the country with a death rate well above that for Germany, Canada, Australia and Italy.

Peter Yuen, author of the OHE Compendium of Health Statistics, said: 'Even if we achieve the target

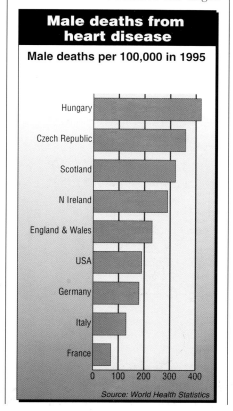

Male deaths from heart disease

Male deaths per 100,000 in 1995

Hungary
Czech Republic
Scotland
N Ireland
England & Wales
USA
Germany
Italy
France

0   100   200   300   400

Source: World Health Statistics

in 10 years, the other countries will have moved on and we will never catch up.'

For breast cancer, Britain's death rate among women aged 35 to 64 'is among the highest in the developed world', the report says. Despite medical advances in treatment in recent decades it says the death rate has changed little in England and Wales and Scotland since 1960 and has 'worsened considerably' in Northern Ireland.

Over the past 25 years, National Health Service spending per head of population has more than doubled in real terms, from £378 in 1973 to £815 in 1998, at today's prices. Total spending on health has risen to £56bn, including £8bn in the private sector, a rise from 4.6 to 6.7 per cent of gross domestic product since 1973. Britain still has one of the least expensive health systems in the world.

'If we were to raise our spending to the level of the Germans at 10.4 per cent of GDP we would have an extra £28bn,' Mr Yuen said. 'But where would we find the money?'

• Total spending per head on NHS and private care in the UK reached £889 in 1997, compared with £2,497 in the US, £1,643 in Germany and £1,433 in France.

Check your healthy heart I.Q.

Answer 'true' or 'false' to the following questions to test your knowledge of heart disease and its risk factors. Be sure to check the answers and explanations at the end to see how well you do.

1. The risk factors for heart disease that you can do something about are: high blood pressure, high blood cholesterol, smoking, obesity, and physical inactivity.

2. A stroke is often the first symptom of high blood pressure, and a heart attack is often the first symptom of high blood cholesterol.

3. A blood pressure greater than or equal to 140/90 mm Hg is generally considered to be high.

4. High blood pressure affects the same number of blacks as it does whites.

5. The best ways to treat and control high blood pressure are to control your weight, exercise, eat less salt (sodium), restrict your intake of alcohol, and take your high blood pressure medicine, if prescribed by your doctor.

6. A blood cholesterol of 240 mg/dL is desirable for adults.

7. The most effective dietary way to lower the level of your blood cholesterol is to eat foods low in cholesterol.

8. Lowering blood cholesterol levels can help people who have already had a heart attack.

9. Only children from families at high risk of heart disease need to have their blood cholesterol levels checked.

10. Smoking is a major risk factor for four of the five leading causes of death including heart attack, stroke, cancer, and lung diseases such as emphysema and bronchitis.

11. If you have had a heart attack, quitting smoking can help reduce your chances of having a second attack.

12. Someone who has smoked for 30 to 40 years probably will not be able to quit smoking.

13. The best way to lose weight is to increase physical activity and eat fewer calories.

14. Heart disease is the leading killer of men and women in the United States.

Answers

1. True
High blood pressure, smoking, and high blood cholesterol are the three most important risk factors for heart disease. On the average, each one doubles your chance of developing heart disease. So, a person who has all three of the risk factors is 8 times more likely to develop heart disease than someone who has none. Obesity increases the likelihood of developing high blood cholesterol and high blood pressure, which increase your risk of heart disease. Physical inactivity increases your risk of heart attack. Regular exercise and good nutrition are essential to reducing high blood pressure, high blood cholesterol, and overweight. People who exercise are also more likely to cut down or stop smoking.

2. True
A person with high blood pressure or high blood cholesterol may feel fine and look great; there are often no signs that anything is wrong until a stroke or heart attack occurs. To find out if you have high blood pressure or high blood cholesterol, you should be tested by a doctor, nurse, or other health professional.

3. True
A blood pressure of 140/90 mm Hg or greater is generally classified as high blood pressure. However, blood pressures that fall below 140/90 mm Hg can sometimes be a problem. If the diastolic pressure, the second or lower number, is between 85-89, a person is at an increased risk for heart disease or stroke and should have his/her blood pressure checked at least once a year by a health professional. The higher your blood pressure, the greater your risk of developing heart disease or stroke. Controlling high blood pressure reduces your risk.

4. False
High blood pressure is more common in blacks than whites. It affects 29

out of every 100 black adults compared to 26 out of every 100 white adults. Also, with ageing, high blood pressure is generally more severe among blacks then among whites, and therefore causes more strokes, heart disease, and kidney failure.

5. *True*
Recent studies show that lifestyle changes can help keep blood pressure levels normal even into advanced age and are important in treating and preventing high blood pressure. Limit high-salt foods which include many snack foods, such as potato chips, salted pretzels, and salted crackers; processed foods, such as canned soups; and condiments, such as ketchup and soy sauce. Also, it is extremely important to take blood pressure medication, if prescribed by your doctor, to make sure your blood pressure stays under control.

6. *False*
A total blood cholesterol of under 200 mg/dL is desirable and usually puts you at a lower risk for heart disease. A blood cholesterol level of 240 mg/dL or above is high and increases your risk of heart disease. If your cholesterol level is high, your doctor will want to check your levels of LDL-cholesterol ('bad' cholesterol) and HDL-cholesterol ('good' cholesterol). A HIGH level of LDL-cholesterol increases your risk for heart disease, as does a LOW level of HDL-cholesterol. A cholesterol level of 200-239 mg/dL is considered borderline-high and usually increases your risk for heart disease. If your cholesterol is borderline-high, you should speak to your doctor to see if additional cholesterol tests are needed. All adults 20 years of age or older should have their blood cholesterol level checked at least once every 5 years.

7. *False*
Reducing the amount of cholesterol in your diet is important; however, eating foods low in saturated fat is the most effective dietary way to lower blood cholesterol levels, along with eating less total fat and cholesterol. Choose low-saturated fat foods, such as grains, fruits, and vegetables; low-fat or skimmed milk and milk products; lean cuts of meat; fish; and chicken. Trim fat from meat before cooking; bake or broil meat rather than fry; use less fat and oil; and take the skin off chicken and turkey. Reducing overweight will also help lower your level of LDL-cholesterol as well as increase your level of HDL- cholesterol.

8. *True*
People who have had one heart attack are at much higher risk for a second attack. Reducing blood cholesterol levels can greatly slow down (and, in some people, even reverse) the build-up of cholesterol and fat in the walls of the arteries and significantly reduce the chances of a second heart attack.

9. *True*
Children from 'high risk' families, in which a parent has high blood cholesterol (240 mg/dL or above) or in which a parent or grandparent has had heart disease at an early age (at 55 years of age or younger), should have their cholesterol levels tested. If a child from such a family has a cholesterol level that is high, it should be lowered under medical supervision, primarily with diet, to reduce the risk of developing heart disease as an adult. For most children, who are not from high-risk families, the best way to reduce the risk of adult heart disease is to follow a low-saturated fat, low cholesterol eating pattern. All children over the age of 2 years and all adults should adopt a heart-healthy eating pattern as a principal way of reducing coronary heart disease.

10. *True*
Heavy smokers are 2 to 4 times more likely to have a heart attack than nonsmokers, and the heart attack death rate among all smokers is 70 per cent greater than that of non-smokers. Older male smokers are also nearly twice as likely to die from stroke than older men who do not smoke, and these odds are nearly as high for older female smokers. Further, the risk of dying from lung cancer is 22 times higher for male smokers than male nonsmokers and 12 times higher for female smokers than female nonsmokers. Finally, 80 per cent of all deaths from emphysema and bronchitis are directly due to smoking.

11. *True*
One year after quitting, ex-smokers cut their extra risk for heart attack by about half or more, and eventually the risk will return to normal in healthy ex-smokers. Even if you have already had a heart attack, you can reduce your chances of a second attack if you quit smoking. Ex-smokers can also reduce their risk of stroke and cancer, improve blood flow and lung function, and help stop diseases like emphysema and bronchitis from getting worse.

12. *False*
Older smokers are more likely to succeed at quitting smoking than younger smokers. Quitting helps relieve smoking-related symptoms like shortness of breath, coughing, and chest pain. Many quit to avoid further health problems and take control of their lives.

13. *True*
Weight control is a question of balance. You get calories from the foods you eat. You burn off calories by exercising. Cutting down on calories, especially calories from fat, is key to losing weight. Combining this with a regular physical activity, like walking, cycling, jogging, or swimming, not only can help in losing weight but also in maintaining weight loss. A steady weight loss of 1/2 to 1 pound a week is safe for most adults, and the weight is more likely to stay off over the long run. Losing weight, if you are overweight, may also reduce your blood pressure, lower your LDL-cholesterol, and raise your HDL-cholesterol. Being physically active and eating fewer calories will also help you control your weight if you quit smoking.

14. *True*
Coronary heart disease is the #1 killer in the United States. Approximately 489,000 Americans died of coronary heart disease in 1990, and approximately half of the deaths were women.
• Information from the National Heart, Lung, and Blood Institute, part of the National Institute of Health.

© *US Department of Health and Human Services*

Early warning test for smokers' hearts

Can the likelihood of cigarette-induced heart disease be predicted?

By Brigid McConville

Few smokers need reminding that cigarettes are bad for their health, but many require stark evidence of their own mortality before they are finally willing to set about quitting the evil weed. However, for those who would prefer to stop short of a heart attack, a new test is available, which claims to tell patients whether they can get away with smoking for a while longer – or whether they should stop instantly.

The Smokescreen, which is being launched in Britain by Dr Rajendra Sharma, medical director of the Hale Clinic, combines blood screening with a Doppler ultrasound test to show whether a person's arteries are clogging up.

'The main hazard for smokers is the formation of a cholesterol plug, or atheroma, in the arteries,' says Dr Sharma. 'The combination of atheroma and free radicals in the blood – which are also created by smoking – can be devastating to the arteries' inner linings.'

According to Dr Sharma, clogged arteries prevent oxygen and nutrients from reaching the major organs, causing the smoker's risk of stroke or heart attack to increase six-fold.

The Smokescreen test assesses the degree of clotting by analysing the blood for anti-oxidant levels. A low reading suggests that the patient will be more vulnerable to damage by free radicals – negatively charged particles that can damage blood vessels, enabling clots to form. The test will also show the level of 'good' fats and 'bad' fats in the blood.

The sound wave section of the Smokescreen test is a non-invasive inspection of the major blood vessels, giving a picture of blood flow (perfusion). If this is diminished, it indicates that atheroma may already be clogging up the arteries.

So what if the test does reveal that your arteries are dangerously clogged up? The obvious first step is to stop smoking, in order to prevent things from getting worse. Dr Sharma also recommends high dose anti-oxidant treatment, both oral and intravenous, to reverse the damage.

> *'The programme allows the doctor to enter standard risk factors – such as cholesterol, blood pressure, smoking and heart health – and calculate an individual's risk of a stroke or heart attack'*

Leading cardiologists at University College London have been working on a similar scare tactic. They have developed an interactive computer programme which shows patients clear visual evidence of their risk of heart disease.

Patrick Vallance, Professor of Clinical Pharmacology and Therapeutics at UCL, says: 'The programme allows the doctor to enter standard risk factors – such as cholesterol, blood pressure, smoking and heart health – and calculate an individual's risk of a stroke or heart attack. It can also show the effect of making changes, such as stopping smoking.'

But if patients are not found to be at immediate risk of heart attack or stroke, don't such tests merely give them an excuse to continue with their habit? Dr Sharma believes that patients who are found to have low levels of free radicals and 'bad' fatty acids may be able to smoke for many years, with relatively little cardio-vascular damage.

'Perhaps 10 per cent of people can get away with smoking,' he concedes. 'But a test result that gives them a time scale, telling them that they have a certain number of months or years before their arteries fur up and they have a stroke, has to be a greater deterrent than a stop-smoking leaflet.'

Smokescreen costs around £299, which, as Dr Sharma points out, amounts to less than three months' supply of cigarettes for a 20-a-day smoker.

• Smokescreen: tel. 01202 716731

Study casts doubt on heart 'risk factors'

By Aisling Irwin,
Science Correspondent

The largest-ever cardiology study has failed to find a link between heart attacks and the classic risk factors, such as smoking and high cholesterol levels.

The Monica study, which assessed 21 countries over 10 years, found the incidence of heart disease dropping across Europe, Australia and North America. But scientists could find no statistical connection between the reduction and changes in obesity, smoking, blood pressure or cholesterol levels.

'Changing rates of coronary heart disease in different populations did not appear to relate at all well to the change in the standard risk factors,' the Monica organisers said in the report published yesterday. 'This will be a big surprise for many people,' said Dr Caroline Morrison, co-principal investigator for the Glasgow contribution to the study.

Public health specialists urged people to continue tackling potential risk factors, pointing out that many other studies had shown that they were linked unequivocally with heart disease. They said the results might give more insight into the difficulties of running trials over huge geographical areas and the unexpected complexity of heart disease than they did about risk factors.

The results were announced at the European Congress of Cardiology in Vienna. The world's largest and longest heart study amassed information about 150,000 heart attacks, mainly in western Europe but also in Russia, Iceland, Canada, China and Australia. The decrease in the incidence of heart disease was greatest in Sweden, at eight per cent, with a modest drop of two per cent in Glasgow, one of the two British centres that took part. Clear increases were recorded in Lithuania, Poland, China and Russia.

Obesity rose around the world, with the average weight increasing by a couple of kilograms over a decade. The greatest increases were in America, Canada, Australia, Iceland and New Zealand, while weight fell in Russia, Lithuania, Czechoslovakia and, among men only, Switzerland.

> **'Changing rates of coronary heart disease in different populations did not appear to relate at all well to the change in the standard risk factors'**

Smoking decreased among men in 32 of the 38 centres but, among women, in only 13 centres. Blood pressure dropped almost everywhere in the study. Cholesterol levels remained the same. But scientists failed to find a correlation between these factors and incidence of heart disease.

The World Health Organisation, which funded Monica, said: 'That the classical risk factors make major contributions to individual risk has been shown repeatedly in numerous studies.'

A possible explanation was that these four risk factors had been swamped by others, said Prof Hugh Tunstall-Pedoe of Dundee University, a member of the Monica steering committee. Unrest, poverty, and social and economic change have all been linked with heart disease since the study began in the early 1980s. Someone who gives up smoking but loses their home may overall be at higher risk of heart disease because of stress.

Eating fruit, vegetables and fish may also play a major role not appreciated – and therefore not recorded – when the study was designed. The study has had many successes, said Dr Morrison. 'Locally, it has produced masses of data which is already being used.'

HEY—THEY CAN'T FIND A LINK BETWEEN SMOKING, OBESITY, BLOOD PRESSURE, OR CHOLESTEROL AND HEART ATTACKS!!

...WE'LL STILL KEEP THE AMBULANCE PHONE NUMBER IN GLOW-IN-THE-DARK LETTERS ABOVE THE TELEPHONE, OKAY...

SIMON KNEEBONE

Women and coronary heart disease

Most people think of men, not women, as having heart attacks. But coronary heart disease is the biggest single cause of death for women in the UK.

Statistics

In 1997, 64,000 women died of coronary heart disease in the UK, compared with 76,500 men.

About 1 in every 4 women in the UK dies from coronary heart disease. Although most of the deaths are women over the age of 65, nearly 6,000 women die each year before the age of 65. Death from coronary heart disease began to fall slightly after the late seventies for both men and women, but deaths among the wives of manual workers have actually increased.

As well as the deaths from coronary heart disease, many thousands of women suffer pain and disability. Although women have fewer heart attacks than men, they are only slightly less likely to suffer from angina – the narrowing of the coronary arteries which can cause a heavy pain across the chest.

Cutting down the risks

It seems likely that most of the risk factors which apply to women: cigarette smoking, high blood pressure, diet and lack of exercise. Women are at particular risk of coronary heart disease if they take the contraceptive pill, and women who smoke and take the pill are ten times more likely to die of a heart attack or stroke than non-smoking women who are not on the pill. Some people have suggested that as more and more women take on paid work, coronary heart disease deaths among women will increase because of work related stress. However, research carried out in the United States found that, in general, women in paid employment had roughly the same rate of coronary heart disease as women working at home. The women who did have a slightly higher risk were those who worked in low-paid clerical jobs.

Women and prevention

Much of the advice on prevention of coronary heart disease has been oriented towards men. Advice to women is usually about what they could do to reduce their husband's or children's risk of coronary heart disease rather than their own.

Healthy eating

Women are often told that in choosing food for the family, they have their family's hearts in their hands. But in reality, husbands and children are often in control – they simply refuse to eat certain foods. Many women end up feeling guilty as they try to reconcile healthy eating advice with their family's habits. And sometimes the only way to avoid a family fight is to give in and give them chips.

Some healthier snacks to try are:
- Low fat crisps, or better still, dried fruit and nuts instead of ordinary sweets.
- Fruit instead of sweets.
- Tea cakes or scones (preferably wholemeal) instead of biscuits.
- Fruit juice instead of fizzy pop.

Smoking

Although millions of people in the UK have given up smoking, men are giving up faster than women. From 1982 to 1992, the percentage of male smokers fell from 38% to 29%, but during the same period, women's smoking only went down from 33% to 28%.

Anti-smoking education for women has often been aimed at pregnant women, and the emphasis is on protecting the baby rather than the woman's health.

Men and women have different reasons for smoking, and different problems when it comes to giving up. One of the biggest problems for women trying to give up is the fear of putting on weight. It seems that women are more likely than men to smoke in order to reduce feelings of anxiety or anger. Some women worry that if they give up smoking they might not be able to suppress their angry feelings.

Overall there is an urgent need for more research into the causes of coronary heart disease in women in order to find more practical ways of helping women to reduce their risks of coronary heart disease.

• The above information is from the Coronary Prevention Group web site which can be found at www.healthnet.org.uk

© The Coronary Prevention Group

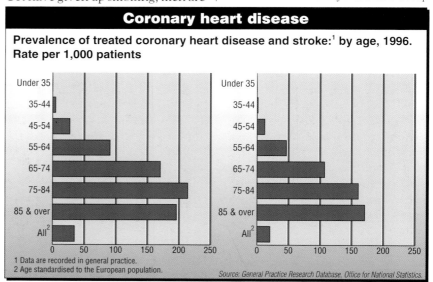

Coronary heart disease

Prevalence of treated coronary heart disease and stroke:[1] by age, 1996. Rate per 1,000 patients

1 Data are recorded in general practice.
2 Age standardised to the European population.

Source: General Practice Research Database, Office for National Statistics.

Heart death rate more than twice European level

By Celia Hall,
Medical Editor

Death rates from heart disease in Britain are more than twice those in comparable European countries and there is little chance of closing the gap, statisticians said yesterday.

The Compendium of Health Statistics puts England and Wales, Scotland, Northern Ireland and Ireland at the top of a list of 14 developed nations, worldwide, for heart disease deaths. In Scottish men, death rates are 320 per 100,000, compared to 125 in the Netherlands, 75 in France and 20 in Japan.

For English women the figure is 60 per 100,000 compared to 25 in Italy and about 15 in France. The figure for America is about 60 for women and just under 200 for men.

The compendium is an annual publication from the Office of Health Economics, a research organisation supported by the British pharma-ceutical industry. About 500 people die on waiting lists for bypass surgery and the Government has set a target of reducing deaths from heart disease and related illness by 40 per cent in people over 75 by 2010.

Adrian Towse, director of the office, said: 'The problem is to ask, at what stage should the health service intervene to be effective? At what point should people be having checks, be treated and be made aware of the risks of smoking and diet?

'People need to get the right treatment at the right time. We would like to see differential targets, a focus on waiting lists for different diseases, rather than concentrating on overall lists.'

The statistics show that total health care spending in the United Kingdom was £56 billion in 1998, of which £8 billion was spent in the private sector. This represents 6.7 per cent of gross domestic product, putting Britain at the bottom of the health spending league in Europe. In Germany health spending is 10.4 per cent of GDP, in France 9.9 per cent and in America 10.4 per cent.

In terms of money spent on health care per head of population, the figure in the United Kingdom was £946 last year compared to £2,497 in America (1997), £1,643 in Germany and £1,433 in France. The figures also show the variation in spending. Health care expenditure in Northern Ireland was £1,009 last year against £858 in Scotland, £790 in Wales and £704 in England.

Glasgow and Belfast top heart attack list

Poor diet, smoking and lack of exercise likely causes of death rate

By Sarah Boseley,
Health Correspondent

Glasgow and Belfast have topped a poll as two cities with some of the worst rates of heart attacks in the world, according to the results of a 10-year study published in the *Lancet*.

The first definitive results of the World Health Organisation's Monica (cardiovascular disease monitoring) project revealed that of 37 centres studied in 21 countries, Glasgow had the worst heart attack rate among women and the second worst among men. Belfast was second and fourth respectively.

The cities across four continents were chosen largely because of their worryingly high rates of heart disease. Only North Karelia, in Finland, long notorious for the high cholesterol levels of its inhabitants, had a worse record for heart attacks in men than Glasgow.

When the study began, said Hugh Tunstall-Pedoe of the cardiovascular epidemiology unit of Dundee University, cholesterol in Finland was extremely high, partly because of the tendency of people on farms to drink two pints of milk a day and partly because they boiled their coffee, which brings out a cholesterol-raising substance from the beans.

Dietary changes have succeeded in bringing cholesterol levels down more steeply than anywhere else, and yet the Finns still top the league table. 'Their decline is very creditable, but I think an awful lot of people are under the impression that Finland has conquered heart disease. That is not the case,' Professor Tunstall-Pedoe said.

Glasgow's problems come from high levels of smoking, and a poor diet causing high cholesterol and blood pressure. The intake of fruit and vegetables, which protect against cancer and heart disease, is low and the population generally does not take enough exercise.

The study reveals a remarkable difference in heart attack rates between northern and southern Europe. Catalonia in Spain and Brianza in Italy have some of the lowest rates. Toulouse, in southern France, is with them, and markedly healthier than either Lille or Strasbourg. An editorial in the *Lancet* by Joseph Alpert of the department of medicine at Arizona University, says this is the so-called 'French paradox'.

Glasgow's problems come from high levels of smoking, and a poor diet causing high cholesterol and blood pressure

---

Heart disease in southern France is low in spite of a diet heavy in cholesterol. But fruit and vegetable consumption is high, and Glasgow University studies have suggested antioxidants called flavonols in fruit, vegetables and red wine may play a part.

The Monica project's aim was to discover whether the fall in deaths in the West was due to a decrease in heart attacks or better medical care for the victims.

The *Lancet* finds that there has been a drop in the number of heart attacks probably because of the increasing Western awareness of the importance of diet and exercise.

But as Western habits spread in some of the developing world, it is becoming clear that heart disease is on the increase there.

© *The Guardian*
May, 1999

Risk factors

Information from Women's Health Interactive – 'A unique learning environment for women'

If you weigh 20% or more over your ideal weight your weight is a risk factor for coronary heart disease. Studies conclude that obesity is a major cause of coronary heart disease among women in the United States.

The Myth: I must attain some 'ideal' weight that seems impossible to achieve.

The Truth: The latest research shows that even if you're very significantly overweight, a loss of as little as fifteen pounds can raise your self-esteem, improve your health, and reduce the probability of your developing heart disease.

A guide to weight loss
Creating a healthier lifestyle clearly includes eating right. The *Woman's Heart Book* gives you a strategy for eating right (drum roll, please): The eating plan you're most likely to stick with is the one closest to the way you normally eat. Perhaps it seems as if the foods you eat daily are mostly chosen at random, i.e., 'There's a muffin shop across from my office, so I start the day with a muffin.' Such choices may actually not be random at all; your food preferences are probably far more deep-seated. After all, when you go 'off' a diet, you automatically revert to your old eating habits. It follows that if your

eating plan is similar to the one you would normally follow it's harder to 'go off it'. So it's a matter of selecting the types of food that are the most healthy while still staying within your normal eating plan.

Compare the way you eat with the US Department of Agriculture's recommendations for a healthy diet. The following menu comes from the USDA's dietary guidelines for both men and women. Since most women require less food than men, you should use the lower number of

suggested servings especially if you want to lose weight.

Lifesaving tip: Lowering the fat in your diet reduces your risk of developing not only coronary artery disease, but also breast cancer and diabetes.

• The above information is an extract from the Women's Health Interactive web site, which can be found at www.womens-health.com

© *Reprinted with the permission of Women's Health Interactive™*

Type of food	Suggested daily servings
Vegetables	3-5 servings (raw, leafy vegetables, 1 cup, other types, 1/2 cup)
Fruits	2-4 servings (i.e. 1 medium apple, 1/2 cup of fruit, or 3/4 cup of juice)
Breads, cereals, rice and pasta	6-11 servings (1 slice of bread, 1/2 bun, bagel, English muffin, 1 ounce of dry cereal, 1/2 cup cooked cereal, rice, or pasta)
Milk, yoghurt, and cheese	2-3 servings (1 serving equals 1 cup of milk or yoghurt or 1/2 ounce of cheese)
Meats, poultry, fish, dry beans and peas, eggs, and nuts	2-3 servings (your daily total should be about 3 ounces. Beef should be lean, and chicken cooked without skin. A 3-ounce portion is about the size of a deck of cards.)

Heart attack risk 'starting to vanish for the rich'

The most affluent men and women in Britain may soon be able to forget their fears of dropping dead of a heart attack, according to a new report yesterday. But without continued efforts to improve the diet, exercise and smoking habits of everybody else, heart disease will still kill and disable vast numbers of the population.

Coronary heart disease is the nation's biggest killer. Around 300,000 have heart attacks every year and half die, including almost 21,000 before the age of 65. Many more suffer disability as a result.

Yesterday, the National Heart Forum published a report on the scale of the epidemic and ways of preventing the disease. Although death rates are falling in Britain, they are not dropping as fast as in Australia or the United States, where strategies for dealing with it were developed a decade earlier than here.

The decline in deaths may be due to improvements in diet, contributors to the report said yesterday. During the 1980s, there was a swing away from whole milk and butter to skimmed milk and polyunsaturated margarines. But there is a substantial gap between the drop in heart attacks among the richest and among the poorest.

Heart attacks among the under-64s in social class one – the most affluent in society – are in steep decline. At the top of the social tree, people are less likely to smoke and more likely to eat their life-enhancing quota of five portions of fruit and vegetables a day.

According to Michael Marmot, professor of epidemiology and public health at University College London, there may be another reason, lack of stress. Stress is a factor in heart disease, he said. But his studies have shown that the most stressed are not affluent executives, but those, often further down the social scale, who do not feel in control of their lives.

By Sarah Boseley, Health Correspondent

But the success in avoiding heart attacks of the richest will not save the NHS from being overwhelmed by heart attack victims in the next few decades. There is a demographic timebomb waiting. Most of those who suffer heart attacks are over 65, and the proportion of older people in the population is rising steeply.

Heart attacks among the under-64s in social class one – the most affluent in society – are in steep decline

Improving the nation's diet is fundamental to preventing heart disease in the population by eating less fat and more fruit and vegetables and wholegrains, said Gerry Shaper, emeritus professor of clinical epidemiology.

Smoking and exercise affect an individual's risk, but an examination for the report of all kinds of possible other factors from obesity to psycho-social factors and air pollution, concluded that diet was more important than anything.

He, and other members of the forum, called for a new food strategy from government.

They want the Food Standards Agency to have the issue of nutrition within its remit and call for a Public Health Agency to be set up to pull together relevant issues, such as school meals, across departments.

Tessa Jowell, minister for public health, said that the report would provide valuable guidance in tackling coronary heart disease and shaping services into the new millennium.

She added: 'It will make an important contribution to the work being done nationally and through local programmes, such as health improvement programmes, healthy living centres, health action zones and the work of the new primary care groups.'

The Government has already pledged itself to cut coronary heart disease deaths by a third by 2010.

© *The Guardian,*
April, 1999

...MONEY DOESN'T BUY EVERYTHING!

...DOES BUY A **LIFE**STYLE...

STRESS

Worldwide trends

Major cardiovascular study shows substantial regional differences

Men living in North Karelia (Finland), Glasgow (United Kingdom), Kuopio (Finland) and Belfast (United Kingdom), and women living in Glasgow (United Kingdom), Belfast (United Kingdom), Newcastle (Australia) and Warsaw (Poland) have the highest average rates of heart disease among 170,000 people studied over a 10-year period from the mid 1980s to the mid 1990s.

The lowest average heart attack rates in women over the ten years occurred in Catalonia (Spain), Beijing (China), Toulouse (France) and Brianza (Italy). Women's heart attack rates in Glasgow were eight times higher than those in Catalonia, for example. Among men, the lowest average heart attack rates over the ten years occurred in Beijing (China), Catalonia (Spain), Vaud-Fribourg (Switzerland) and Toulouse (France); rates in North Karelia were ten times higher than those in Beijing, for example.

These are just some of the findings from the World Health Organisation (WHO)-sponsored 'Monica' (from MONItoring CArdiovascular disease) Project which studied 170 thousand heart attacks around the world over a 10-year period to get an accurate picture of cardiovascular disease levels and trends.

The first findings from this, the world's largest ever study of heart disease, are being published in the *Lancet* (a United Kingdom medical journal) on 8 May 1999. The Monica Project tracked heart attack rates, risk factors and coronary care in pre-defined populations in 37 countries from the mid 1980s to the mid 1990s.

The greatest fall in coronary event rates in men occurred in three north European populations: the leader being North Karelia, Finland (which had the highest levels at the start of the study), Kuopio (also in Finland) and Northern Sweden. These three regions were followed by Newcastle (Australia). With the exception of Catalonia (Spain), male populations experiencing notable increase in rates were predominantly from central and eastern Europe and Asia. In women, the populations experiencing significant increases again tended to be from central and eastern Europe and Asia, but the general pattern of increases and decreases appeared to be less consistent.

'Cardiovascular disease – largely heart attacks and strokes – is the leading cause of death in the world today and will remain so by the year 2020'

Trends in heart attack rates were similar to those in the routine mortality statistics, even though the latter tended to underestimate death rates from coronary disease in many countries. The WHO Monica Project thus validates the use of routine death data for monitoring long-term trends in death from heart disease.

Where mortality rates were falling, change in survival contributed one-third and change in heart attack rates two-thirds, on average, of the total change in survival rates, indicating the importance of both the prevention of heart disease and improved care of acute events.

The lead author of the report was Professor Hugh Tunstall-Pedoe of the Cardiovascular Epidemiology Unit of Dundee University at Ninewells Hospital, Scotland. He worked with Dr Kari Kuulasmaa, Chief Scientist of the Monica Project and three of his colleagues from the Monica Data Centre in the National Public Health Institute, Helsinki, Finland, and with Professor Philippe Amouyel from the Pasteur Institute of Lille in France.

Professor Amouyel stressed that, 'The WHO Monica study paid great attention to standardisation of diagnosis and procedures and to measuring and reporting the performance of the different centres. For the sake of scientific transparency, our procedures and quality control tests, the individual results and the overall scores are being simultaneously published on the internet' (http://www.ktl.fi/publications/monica).

Professor Tunstall-Pedoe said, 'This is one of a series of major reports from the WHO Monica Project. Later ones, in preparation, cover issues such as how much changes in medical treatment and in coronary risk factors are responsible for the changes recorded here in survival and event rates.'

'Cardiovascular disease – largely heart attacks and strokes – is the leading cause of death in the world today and will remain so by the year 2020. The WHO Monica Project is a cause for optimism: heart attack rates are declining in most Monica centres and there is no reason why these improvements cannot be continued and extended to other countries. WHO has given priority to the prevention and control of cardiovascular diseases, and non-communicable diseases more generally as an indication of its desire to accelerate these favourable trends,' said Dr Ruth Bonita, Director of Non-communicable Disease Surveillance at WHO.

• The above information is from the World Health Organisation (WHO).

About heart, stress and blood pressure

Your heart is the motor that drives you through life. If it's well cared for you can cruise along without a care, largely untroubled by faults or failures. But if it's neglected and not given the right fuel, it can't do its job properly and may break down altogether. Controlling stress levels and cholesterol through a healthy diet is crucial to the well-being of your heart. We show you how.

Coronary heart disease

Coronary heart disease is the most common cause of death in the UK: more than 140,000 people die from it each year and around 2 million more show significant signs of heart disease. Factors affecting heart disease include high blood pressure, stress, excess cholesterol, and an unhealthy lifestyle, particularly excess drinking, smoking, too many fats in the diet, and not enough exercise.

Blood pressure control

High blood pressure or hypertension is one of several things which can increase your risk of heart disease or stroke. The trouble is you can't tell if you have high blood pressure unless it is measured. You may only find out as part of a general health check by your doctor or nurse. It's a good idea to have your blood pressure checked regularly when you see your doctor.

These days it is also possible to buy blood pressure monitors to use at home. There are a number of monitors available at Boots, all providing quick, accurate results using up-to-date technology.

Causes of stress

Almost anything can cause stress, however, one of the most common causes of stress is change – in your daily routine, your job, where you live or your relationships. It isn't the actual change that really matters though, it's your approach to it. The best way to reduce any stress caused by change is to try and adapt to the situation rather than fight against it.

Healthy eating for your heart

We now know that our diet can play a major role in keeping our heart in peak condition. It makes sense to eat a healthy diet. This can be done in various ways.

- Choose foods which are labelled 'low fat'.
- Eat more pulses such as peas, beans and lentils.
- Choose lean cuts of meat and trim off all the visible fat before cooking.
- Increase your fibre intake by starting your day with a high-fibre cereal.
- As too much salt contributes towards high blood pressure, cut down on the amount you sprinkle on your food or add to your cooking. There are several 'Low Salt' seasoning products available.
- Try to cut down on the amount of alcohol you drink. Alcohol tends to increase blood pressure, making it harder for the heart to pump blood around the body. Today there are many excellent low and non-alcoholic drinks available, so it's easy to find a sociable alternative. Not only will

you have fewer calories to count but you'll also have a healthier heart.

Controlling cholesterol

Cholesterol is a waxy, yellow-white substance produced mostly in the liver. One of its main jobs is to help produce the substances we need to digest the fats that we eat. Cholesterol is also needed by every cell in our body. It helps to insulate our nerves, make Vitamin D, and to build some of the hormones we need to live.

Our liver makes cholesterol in response to the amount and type of fat we eat. If we eat too much of the wrong type of fat, high levels of cholesterol can build up in the blood. Cholesterol helps to carry digested fat through our blood system to the cells where it is needed. But since fat and water don't mix (and blood is mostly water) our body needs to parcel up the cholesterol and other fats with soluble substances called lipoproteins. There are several types of lipoproteins.

Low Density Lipoproteins (LDLs)

The liver sends out the LDLs (bad lipoproteins) with their load of cholesterol to distribute around our body. On their journey some of these LDLs can leave their cholesterol stuck along the walls of the blood

13

vessels, making them narrower. If this happens in the blood vessels of the heart it can cause serious problems.

High Density Lipoproteins (HDLs)

It is the job of the HDLs (good lipoproteins) to try and remove the 'stuck' cholesterol and carry it back to the liver to be recycled or disposed of.

Measuring levels

You don't have to know your cholesterol level to keep your heart in good health. But studies have shown that about two-thirds of people in the UK have levels higher than recommended, so knowing your level can be quite helpful. If it is high it will give the chance to take steps to lower it, and you'll be able to see how successful you've been the next time you have a test.

Testing levels

At Boots we have an easy-to-use self-testing kit: The Boots Home Cholesterol Test. This kit contains all you need to test a few drops of your blood for cholesterol. It takes just a few minutes to do the test and you'll know your blood cholesterol level in about 20 minutes.

Each test has a leaflet which explains what the ideal level for blood cholesterol is, and suggests things you can do if your level is higher than recommended.

High levels

If you find your level is especially high, you will need to visit your doctor for further advice. Heart problems tend to run in families, so if you find you have a high cholesterol level and you know that a close relative has had heart trouble before the age of 60, then a visit to your doctor is even more important.

If you smoke or you know you have a high blood pressure, or you suffer from diabetes, then it is always best to let your doctor know that you have tested your cholesterol level and let him know the result.

© *Boots the Chemist*

Heart terms explained

Information from the British Heart Foundation (BHF)

ACE inhibitors
Drugs used for treating high blood pressure

Arteries
The tubes that take the blood away from the heart to the rest of the body

Atherosclerosis
A build-up of fatty materials in the walls of the arteries

Atria
The small upper filling chambers of the heart

Beta-blocker
A drug used to reduce the frequency of angina

Blood pressure
Pressure of blood in the arteries

Calcium antagonists
A drug used to reduce the frequency of angina

Cardiac
Of the heart

Cardiac catheterisation
A fine tube (catheter) is passed through an artery in either the forearm or groin, to the coronary arteries

Cardiologist
Doctor specialising in the heart

Catheter
A fine tube

Coronary angiogram
A test to show where the arteries are narrowed and how narrow they have become

Coronary angioplasty
A treatment to improve the blood supply to the heart muscle. A catheter (fine tube) with a small inflatable balloon at its tip is inserted into an artery in the groin and threaded through the narrowed artery. The balloon is then inflated so that it squashes the fatty tissue responsible for the narrowing, and widens the artery

Coronary artery bypass surgery
An operation to bypass narrowed sections of the coronary arteries

Diastolic blood pressure
The lowest blood pressure, which occurs when the heart is resting between beats

Discharge rate
The rate at which electrical impulses are generated

Dual chamber pacemaker
Pacemaker with two electrical leads: one to the right atrium and one to the right ventricle

ECG (electrocardiogram)
A test to record the electrical activity of the heart

Hypertension
High blood pressure

Left ventricular hypertrophy
When the left ventricle becomes abnormally large and less efficient

Nitrates
Drugs that help to dilate narrowed arteries

Palpitation
The uncomfortable awareness of the heart beat

Stent
A small support frame placed inside the artery to reduce the chance of the artery renarrowing

Systolic blood pressure
The highest blood pressure, which occurs at the time of the contraction of the heart

Thallium scan
A test which involves injecting a small amount of radioactive material into the blood while the person is doing an exercise test

Transvenousvia
A vein

Ventricles
The two larger pumping chambers of the heart

• The above information is from the British Heart Foundation, see page 41 for their address details.

© *British Heart Foundation, 1999*

Coronary artery bypass graft

Information from BUPA's web site

What is a coronary artery bypass graft?

A coronary artery bypass graft (CABG) is an operation to restore or improve the blood flow to the heart muscle. It is performed in special centres.

What are the reasons for having coronary artery bypass graft?

The heart is a special type of muscle that is supplied with blood by several blood vessels called coronary arteries. If these arteries are narrowed, your heart can be starved of blood, which causes pain in the chest called angina. Angina usually occurs when the heart needs more blood, for example, when exercising, but some people have chest pain even when they are resting. These people are at particular risk of a heart attack because the arteries are almost blocked. Many people who have angina only need tablets to control their symptoms. However, some people, despite taking several different types of drugs for angina, have symptoms which make them unable to carry out their normal daily activities. In these cases a CABG is required.

What happens during a coronary artery bypass graft?

At the start of the operation, the surgeon removes a long vein from the leg, which will be used to bypass the coronary arteries that are narrowed. Next, a cut is made in the breast bone to allow the surgeon to work on the heart. As it is not possible for the surgeon to insert this vein while the heart is beating, a special machine is used to add oxygen to the blood and then pump it around the body. Once the machine is running, the heart is stopped and the surgery is performed. Sections of the leg vein are stitched into place, to bypass the narrowings in the coronary arteries, and so allow the blood to flow to the heart muscle. Once this is completed, the heart is restarted and the breast bone stitched together with wire stitches.

What happens before a coronary artery bypass graft?

If your doctor feels that you may need to have a coronary artery bypass, he or she will refer you to a heart specialist. The specialist performs some blood tests and electrical tests to assess your heart. The next step is to find where the blockages in the coronary arteries are, which is done using a dye test known as an angiogram.

A fine tube is inserted into a large artery in the groin or arm and passed towards the heart. Dye is squirted down the tube and special X-rays are taken to show where the dye is held up and hence where the blood vessels that supply the heart muscle are narrowed. Based on these tests, the surgeon decides whether a bypass operation is the appropriate treatment.

It may be possible to open up the narrowings of the artery using a method called 'angioplasty', which does not require an operation and is often considered first.

What should I expect in the hospital?

If the surgeon decides that you need a bypass, you will probably be asked to attend a clinic at which your fitness for the operation is assessed. You will be asked to arrive at the hospital the day before the operation. An anaesthetist (the doctor who puts you to sleep for the operation) will come and meet you before the operation to ensure that he or she is aware of any past medical problems that you have experienced. Before the operation, you will be asked to sign a consent form to say that you understand the procedure and have given your permission for it to be done. You will not be allowed to eat or drink for at least 6 hours before the operation. Your chest and legs will be shaved in preparation and medication may be given to you to make you drowsy before the anaesthetic is administered.

What are the possible common complications of a coronary artery bypass graft?

The operation is generally successful and has a low rate of complications. The most significant complication of a bypass is a stroke, which occurs in up to one in 50 patients. The risk of having a heart attack during the operation is also around one in 50. Other complications include wound infections, chest infections

and abnormal heart rhythms, which usually return to normal after several days. Although the operation reduces or cures angina for most people, in a few the symptoms may return in time and may require further treatment.

How long will I have to stay in hospital?

The operation takes two to three hours, after which you are transferred to an intensive care unit. You will probably wake up three to four hours after the operation has been completed and, providing there are no problems, you will usually leave

> *If the surgeon decides that you need a bypass, you will probably be asked to attend a clinic at which your fitness for the operation is assessed*

the intensive care unit within the next few days. Recovery from the operation is usually straightforward. Pain in the breast bone is common, but usually only for the first few days.

What happens after a coronary artery bypass graft?

Driving is not recommended for four to six weeks afterwards and commercial licence holders need to inform the DVLA of their operation. Although you may feel well soon after the operation, a 2–3 month period of convalescence is usually recommended.

• The above information is an extract from the BUPA web site which can be found at www.bupa.co.uk

You and your heart

Information from The Coronary Prevention Group

Your heart is a pump made of strong muscle. It beats 60-90 times every minute – that's about 100,000 beats every day, or 3,000,000 beats a month. Blood is pumped from the right side of the heart to the lungs where it takes up oxygen. It then returns to the left side, is pumped out through the arteries to carry oxygen to the rest of the body and then returns through the veins to the right side of the heart to start the cycle again.

What is coronary heart disease?

Coronary heart disease usually begins with atherosclerosis – the narrowing of the coronary arteries that carry blood to the heart.

A heart attack happens when there is a sudden blockage in one of those arteries, cutting off the blood supply to the heart muscle. The blockage may be caused by artherosclerosis, or by a blood clot forming (a thrombosis), or by a combination of artherosclerosis and thrombosis.

Sometimes artherosclerosis can cause angina, a severe pain in the chest which can spread to the neck and arms. The pain is like a 'cramp' in the heart muscles, caused when they do not get enough oxygen. This usually happens during a period of exertion or stress and is normally relieved by resting.

What causes coronary heart disease?

The main factors which can increase the risk of coronary heart disease are:
- cigarette smoking
- high blood pressure (hypertension)
- an unhealthy diet
- lack of exercise
- obesity and diabetes
- a family history of coronary heart disease
- stress.

How big is the problem?

Coronary heart disease rates in the UK are among the highest in the world. One in three men and one in four women die from the disease. In 1993, over 90,000 men and 76,000 women died of coronary heart disease. That is 19 people every hour.

Every year 70 million working days are lost because of illnesses associated with coronary heart disease and the NHS spends £900 million each year on treating coronary heart disease.

Death rates from coronary heart disease in the UK are amongst the worst in the world. Until the late seventies coronary heart disease rates in the UK had been steadily rising.

Now the increase in deaths has levelled off and there is evidence of a slight decrease in deaths particularly among young men.

In other countries, broadly comparable in lifestyle with the UK, deaths from coronary heart disease have shown more dramatic improvement.

In the USA and Australia, for example, death rates have fallen by over 32% in the last 15 years compared with 22% in the UK.

It is a common myth that people of a higher social status are more likely to develop coronary heart disease.

In fact people on a low income are more susceptible. Deaths from coronary heart disease are at least twice as high in manual as non-manual workers.

The problem of heart disease is so widespread in the UK that we have to start thinking of coronary heart disease as a public health issue; a problem that could affect us all. Seeing health as a collective effort is a crucial part of effective coronary heart disease prevention.

Set your heart on eating well

Cholesterol has a bad name – but, says Barbara Lantin, it can help as well as hinder the body's fight against disease

Cholesterol is one of those health buzzwords that creates as much confusion as it does reassurance. We know we should strive for low levels, but just how low should we go? Should we all be tested? Can diet alone make a real difference? Do garlic, fish oils and vitamin supplements help? And just how many eggs can we safely eat each week?

Coronary heart disease (CHD) is the most common cause of death in the UK, killing one in four men and one in five women, many of them prematurely. The risk factors are well-known: smoking, physical inactivity, high blood pressure, diabetes, a family history and raised blood cholesterol.

Although adult death rates from heart disease in Britain have fallen by 42 per cent in the past 10 years, they remain among the highest in the world.

Our cholesterol levels are also alarming: an average of 5.8mmol/l (millimols per litre), compared with China's 3.2. A level of 5mmol/l is considered desirable. Yet more than one third of Britons aged 35-64 have a cholesterol level higher than 6.5.

'The average cholesterol level in a population is the main determining factor for rates of CHD,' says John Betteridge, professor of endocrinology and metabolism at University College Hospital, London.

France is the exception, with relatively high average cholesterol level, but a lower than expected incidence of CHD. 'The reason for this is not fully understood, though the Mediterranean diet may play a part,' says Prof Betteridge.

Numerous trials have demonstrated that lowering blood cholesterol reduces heart disease. The famous 1994 Scandinavian 4-S study involving 4,444 people with heart disease showed that there were 30 per cent fewer deaths among those taking statins, the cholesterol-lowering drug marketed as Zocor, than among those on placebo.

Lowering the blood cholesterol level by one per cent decreases the risk of CHD by two to three per cent over a lifetime. So how can we cut our cholesterol and, with it, our chances of succumbing to heart disease?

Contrary to popular belief, most cholesterol in the blood does not come directly from the food on our plate, but is manufactured in the liver from saturated fats. The two main sources of dietary cholesterol – which does come direct from food – are offal and egg yolks.

Cholesterol plays a vital role in the functioning of cell walls and in the manufacture of chemicals in the body. It is transported around the body via the bloodstream by proteins. This combination of cholesterol and protein is called a lipoprotein.

Not all cholesterol is bad. Low-density lipoproteins (LDL), the so-called 'bad' cholesterol, carry cholesterol from the liver to the cells. If there is more circulating than the body needs, it is eventually deposited in the artery walls, leading to 'furring'. High-density lipoproteins (HDL) are known as 'good' cholesterol because they return cholesterol to the liver, where it can be excreted via bile acids.

HDL has a protective effect against heart disease and a high level is desirable. By contrast, high levels of LDL are associated with atherosclerosis – the narrowing of the coronary arteries by a build-up of fatty material called atheroma.

The role of diet in controlling cholesterol remains controversial. 'The most common cause of high blood cholesterol levels in people in the UK is too much fat in the diet,' says the British Heart Foundation. Accordingly, the Government is committed to cutting our fat consumption by around five per cent over the next five years.

However, studies are inconclusive. In a recent trial at Stanford University, California, volunteers' cholesterol levels fell only when their low-fat diet was combined with exercise. Other studies, where the volunteers' diets were very closely controlled, have produced more encouraging results.

'Diet can help reduce cholesterol by up to 10 per cent,' says Prof Betteridge. 'If you could lower the entire population's levels, the overall benefit would be great.

'However, individuals vary tremendously. Some respond very well to low-fat diets but others do not; it is likely that genetic factors largely determine how people respond.'

The basic rules are these: less fat, particularly saturated fat, and more fruit and vegetables, oily fish and soluble fibre. As dietary cholesterol does not have a significant effect on blood levels, eggs need not be banned, but should be limited to three a week.

It is never too late – or too early – to make changes, says Belinda Linden, the cardiac nurse adviser at the British Heart Foundation. 'Altering your diet may not cause fatty deposits in the arteries to disappear but it will stop more developing. As for children, there's a lot of evidence that dietary habits are laid down in childhood. Fatty deposits can start to develop in the early teens, so what children are eating by then matters.'

There is also evidence that mothers with raised cholesterol may pass on problems to their unborn children.

Fat should form no more than 35 per cent of your total energy consumption and saturated fat, which increases cholesterol levels, no more than a third of this. If you eat 2,000 calories a day, allow yourself about 70 grams of fat. There is good evidence from population studies that a diet rich in fruit and vegetables lowers the risk of heart disease.

An important paper published last year looked at five major Western studies covering 11 years and 76,000 people. It found that vegetarians had lower blood cholesterol than meat eaters and were 24 per cent less likely to die from heart disease.

It is thought that, among many other benefits, the antioxidant properties of fruit and vegetables defend the cells against dangerous oxygen-derived free radicals and prevent oxidation, the chemical process that creates atheroma in the artery walls. However, the evidence for antioxidant dietary supplements such as vitamins A, C and E, selenium and betacarotene is less convincing.

Another vitamin often promoted for heart health is B3 or niacin. Both Patrick Holford, founder of the Institute for Optimum Nutrition and health writer Robert Kowalski enthusiastically endorse the cholesterol balancing powers of niacin in their books.

As for children, there's a lot of evidence that dietary habits are laid down in childhood. Fatty deposits can start to develop in the early teens, so what children are eating by then matters'

Lee Hooper of the British Dietetic Association, specialises in heart health. She agrees that niacin can be effective in large doses, but warns: 'At the very high doses recommended, it acts more like a drug than a food supplement and has side-effects including itching, flushing and an elevation in liver enzymes similar to the statins.'

Although not primarily a cholesterol-lowering agent, omega-3 fatty acids found in oily fish such as herring, mackerel, sardines, salmon, fresh tuna, trout and anchovies have been found to reduce death rates in patients at high risk of heart disease.

Mrs Hooper advises everybody to eat one portion of oily fish a week. Those with heart disease should increase this to two or three portions or a daily capsule of an omega-3 supplement. However, children and those of reproductive age should limit their intake in the light of recent fears about raised levels of environmental pollutants in oily fish. Another way to get the essential fatty acids is by eating eggs from hens that are fed on an omega-3 rich diet.

Soluble dietary fibre can reduce LDL by increasing the secretion of bile acids, which are made in the liver from cholesterol. Good sources are oats, fruit and psyllium seeds. From time to time, various other foods have been said to possess miraculous cholesterol-lowering properties, most notably garlic. Once again, the data is confusing. Two trial reviews indicated that garlic lowered cholesterol by nine per cent and 12 per cent respectively.

However, a trial based on 150 subjects published last month showed only a three per cent fall – within the margin of error and no better than that of the placebo group. There was no evidence that the garlic reduced the tendency of cholesterol to become oxidised.

The latest food to take the spotlight is soya. America's Food and Drug Administration recently allowed food manufacturers to make claims about soya's cholesterol-lowering properties. Again, Lee Hooper is sceptical. 'Conclusive evidence is lacking,' she says.

Diet is not the only factor influencing cholesterol. Although some thin people do have raised levels, being overweight raises LDL and increases the risk of heart disease. Therefore, doctors usually advise heart patients to bring their weight within normal limits. Regular daily exercise such as brisk walking, cycling or swimming, is beneficial in raising HDL levels.

All these measures are likely to benefit a vast majority of the population and could well make a difference to some high-risk patients. But if they fail, statins can lower LDS levels by up to 60 per cent and have a dramatic effect on heart attack rates. Although expensive, they are good value for high-risk patients. If you have had a coronary and are not on a statin, ask your GP why.

Coronary heart disease and stroke

An extract from the Government's White Paper, *Saving Lives: Our Healthier Nation*

Target: to reduce the death rate from coronary heart disease and stroke and related diseases in people under 75 years by at least two-fifths by 2010 – saving up to 200,000 lives in total

One group of diseases kills more commonly than any other, can strike within minutes and singles out people in their prime as well as in later life. Coronary heart disease and stroke, along with other diseases of the circulatory system, account for over 200,000 of the half a million deaths which occur in this country each year. And while death rates are improving substantially for the best-off in society, the worst-off have not benefited to anything like the same extent, thus widening the health gap. Many families in our country have experienced the tragedy that these diseases can bring.

In this White Paper all references to coronary heart disease and stroke should be understood to cover all diseases of the circulatory system.

Many more people who survive acute heart attacks and strokes suffer long-term pain and disability. They and their families know how difficult it is to cope with these consequences. Never feeling completely well, unable to work, often confined to the house, constantly reliant on others – these are some of the worst features which many people must endure.

How do we compare?

Death rates for coronary heart disease and stroke fell during the 1970s and 1980s in most Western countries and England was no exception. Deaths from coronary heart disease dropped by 38 per cent between the early 1970s and late 1990s and from stroke by 54 per cent over the same period. But across the European Union (EU), England has one of the worst rates of

coronary heart disease – for people aged under 65 years, we are two and a half times worse than France (the country with the lowest rate in the EU) amongst men and over four times worse for women. For stroke, at least in those aged under 65 years, the picture is rather better with our death rates in men being better than for many other EU countries, but for women our rate is closer to the average and is more than 50 per cent higher than France, the best-performing EU country.

Causes

Several of the major risk factors which increase the chances of people developing coronary heart disease or having a stroke are now well established. The key lifestyle risk factors, shared by coronary heart disease and stroke, are smoking, poor nutrition, obesity, physical inactivity and high blood pressure. Excess alcohol intake is an important additional risk factor for stroke. Many of these risk factors are unevenly spread across society, with poorer people often exposed to the highest risks.

Smoking is the most important modifiable risk factor for coronary heart disease in young and old. The

fact that smokers of whatever age, sex or ethnic group have a higher risk of heart attacks than non-smokers has been known for a quarter of a century. All these effects have also been demonstrated in those exposed to other people's smoke (passive smoking). A lifetime non-smoker is 60 per cent less likely than a current smoker to have coronary heart disease and 30 per cent less likely to suffer a stroke.

While the proportion of young people starting to smoke is similar across social classes, by their 30s half of the better-off young people have stopped smoking while three-quarters of those in the lowest income group carry on. This is powerful evidence of how the cycle of social disadvantage contributes directly to the risk of premature death, avoidable illness and disability. About one-third of smokers are concentrated in the bottom ten per cent of earners in this country. Smoking rates for those in professional social classes have fallen more rapidly than those for the unskilled. For example, in 1972, unskilled men were twice as likely to smoke as professional men; latest figures show that they are now three times as likely to smoke.

Poor diet – containing too much

fat and salt and not enough fruit and vegetables – is another important cause of coronary heart disease and stroke. A diet high in fat, for example, raises cholesterol levels in the blood. A ten per cent reduction in cholesterol lowers the risk of coronary heart disease by 50 per cent at age 40 years falling to 20 per cent at age 70 years. Poor diet is a fact of life for many poorer families. They do not always enjoy easy access to shops selling a variety of affordable foods, which most of us take for granted.

Keeping physically active provides strong protection against coronary heart disease and stroke. It also has beneficial effects on weight control, blood pressure and diabetes – all of which are risk factors in their own right; protects against brittle bones and maintains muscle power; and increases people's general sense of well-being. Levels of physical activity vary by social group and occupation. People in unskilled occupations are more physically active at work but less so in their leisure time than people in professional occupations. Even so, across all social groups we do too little exercise. Six out of ten men and seven out of ten women are not physically active enough to benefit their health.

High blood pressure raises significantly the chances of someone having a stroke or developing coronary heart disease. A modest reduction of salt in the diet, reduction in excess alcohol intake or an increase in physical activity could greatly reduce the risk of stroke and significantly reduce the risk of coronary heart disease. Many people with high blood pressure go unrecognised or are treated ineffectively. These people remain at increased risk.

There are influences in very early childhood, including while a baby is still in the womb, which determine a person's risk of developing coronary heart disease later in life. For example, small size at birth is an important risk factor for coronary heart disease in adult life. Some argue that these influences are related to nutrition.

There is mounting evidence of the impact of the underlying causes of coronary heart disease such as income differences. In countries with greater income inequality, health inequality is greater too. And there is evidence that social stress, reflected in the extent to which an individual has low control over his or her job, increases the risk of coronary heart disease and of premature death. Similarly the degree of social cohesion, the strength of social networks in a community and the nature of people's work may all affect their risk of dying from coronary heart disease.

Action: reducing risk and staying healthy

A number of big changes would put people at much reduced risk of developing coronary heart disease or stroke in the future:

- major changes in diet, particularly among the worst-off, with increased consumption of such foods as fruit, vegetables, and oily fish
- large reductions in tobacco smoking particularly among young people, women and people in disadvantaged communities
- people keeping much more physically active – by walking briskly or cycling, for example – on a regular basis
- people controlling their body weight so as to keep to the right level for their physique
- avoiding drinking alcohol to excess

Deciding not to smoke is choosing life against chronic ill-health and premature death. Giving up smoking produces benefits even in those who have smoked for many years. The White Paper *Smoking Kills* set out our policies for addressing this major cause of stroke and coronary heart disease. In addition to a new three-year public education campaign costing up to £50 million, a network of smoking cessation services will be established around the country, initially in deprived areas known as Health Action Zones. £60 million over three years has been set aside for this vital service. Addiction to nicotine underlies the smoking epidemic and is the reason why people find it so difficult to stop smoking. There is good scientific evidence that a combination of behavioural support and nicotine replacement therapy substantially increases the chances of an ex-smoker remaining free from this addiction. On 17 June we published regulations which set out our intention to ban tobacco advertising with effect from 10 December 1999.

Action: more effective treatment

Early effective treatment of people who are in high-risk groups or who have the initial signs of circulatory disease can prevent or delay them developing full-blown heart attacks or strokes. Experience shows that people's access to effective treatment is very variable across the country.

Although we want to prevent as many cases of coronary heart disease as possible, we want to ensure that people who could benefit from operations to relieve their symptoms are able to gain access to these specialist services. In the past we have also seen inequality in access to coronary bypass operations or

angioplasty according to where someone happens to live. These operations do not always prolong life but they do improve quality of life, relieve the pain of angina and allow people to live free of disability.

Over time we want to ensure that the standards of the best services in the country apply to all parts of the country. That is why we are producing a National Service Framework for Coronary Heart Disease. The framework will set national standards and define service models for health promotion, disease prevention, diagnosis, treatment, rehabilitation and care. It will reduce variations in health care and improve service quality and will be published shortly.

National service frameworks are also planned for older people and for those with diabetes. These will also help to reduce the impact of stroke as well as coronary heart disease. These national service frameworks will be published in April 2000 and April 2001 respectively.

We are also taking action to improve the control of high blood pressure in the population – too many people remain at risk of heart attack or stroke because their high blood pressure is undetected or treated inadequately.

To reduce high blood pressure we will:

- through publication of a review of the evidence, promote good practice in GP referrals
- develop an alcohol strategy for publication during 1999
- review the way that high blood pressure is detected and brought under control
- in partnership with the food industry explore the scope for reducing the salt content of processed foods.

Integrated action

In our fight against coronary heart disease and stroke we can be successful only if everyone recognises that:

- A whole-generation approach is needed to reduce the impact of such factors as smoking, poor nutrition, obesity and physical inactivity by addressing the importance of influences that operate before birth through

healthy pregnancy; laying the foundations for healthy values in early childhood; reinforcing knowledge about risks among young people and equipping them with the skills to take action; helping ensure that in middle and later life people's personal behaviour continues to promote their health and well-being

- Tackling underlying social, economic and environmental conditions is vital. Those factors operate independently as well as through the specific lifestyle factors. So health inequality can be reduced only by giving more people better education; creating employment so that people can achieve greater prosperity; building social capital by increasing social cohesion and reducing social stress by regenerating neighbourhoods and communities; and tackling those aspects of the workplace which are damaging to health

- More effective, high-quality health services have an important part to play by providing support and advice to people who want to reduce the risks to their health; slowing disease progression in people with early signs and symptoms; limiting long-term incapacity for people who have been ill by well-targeted rehabilitation and follow-up care.

We will create an integrated strategy for action to reduce the burden of coronary heart disease and stroke through a contract for health. It will identify what the individual

citizen must do, what local partnerships will do and what action we will take across Government.

Our Healthy Citizens initiative will help us in this task, through NHS Direct; through our Health Skills programme – including training for members of the public in the use of defibrillators; and through our Expert Patients programme which will enable people with vascular disease to manage their own condition.

We shall bring together the implementation of this contract for coronary heart disease and stroke with the implementation of the National Service Framework for Coronary Heart Disease by setting up a high-level Task Force, accountable to the Chief Medical Officer. The Task Force will ensure that the essential groundwork is laid to set us on course for achieving our target for saving lives which would otherwise be lost to coronary heart disease and stroke. We will identify someone of national prominence to act as its champion, whose function will be to build and maintain momentum for action, to communicate the purpose of the contract and to encourage individuals to commit themselves to it.

We will use the Public Health Development Fund to support the achievement of our target for coronary heart disease and stroke.

- The above is an extract from the Government's White Paper *Saving Lives: our healthier nation.*

Facts about heart failure

Information from the US Department of Health and Human Services

What is heart failure?

Heart failure occurs when the heart loses its ability to pump enough blood through the body. Usually, the loss in pumping action is a symptom of an underlying heart problem, such as coronary artery disease.

The term heart failure suggests a sudden and complete stop of heart activity. But, actually, the heart does not suddenly stop. Rather, heart failure usually develops slowly, often over years, as the heart gradually loses its pumping ability and works less efficiently. Some people may not become aware of their condition until symptoms appear years after their heart began its decline.

How serious the condition is depends on how much pumping capacity the heart has lost. Nearly everyone loses some pumping capacity as he or she ages. But the loss is significantly more in heart failure and often results from a heart attack or other disease that damages the heart.

The severity of the condition determines the impact it has on a person's life. At one end of the spectrum, the mild form of heart failure may have little effect on a person's life; at the other end, severe heart failure can interfere with even simple activities and prove fatal. Between those extremes, treatment often helps people lead full lives.

But all forms of heart failure, even the mildest, are a serious health problem, which must be treated. To improve their chance of living longer, patients must take care of themselves, see their physician regularly, and closely follow treatments.

Is there only one type of heart failure?

The term congestive heart failure is often used to describe all patients with heart failure. In reality, congestion (the build-up of fluid) is just one feature of the condition and does not occur in all patients. There are two main categories of heart failure

although within each category, symptoms and effects may differ from patient to patient. The two categories are:

- Systolic heart failure – This occurs when the heart's ability to contract decreases. The heart cannot pump with enough force to push a sufficient amount of blood into the circulation. Blood coming into the heart from the lungs may back up and cause fluid to leak into the lungs, a condition known as pulmonary congestion.
- Diastolic heart failure – This occurs when the heart has a problem relaxing. The heart cannot properly fill with blood because the muscle has become stiff, losing its ability to relax. This form may lead to fluid accumulation, especially in the feet, ankles, and legs. Some patients may have lung congestion.

What causes heart failure?

As stated, the heart loses some of its blood-pumping ability as a natural consequence of ageing. However, a number of other factors can lead to a potentially life-threatening loss of pumping activity.

As a symptom of underlying heart disease, heart failure is closely associated with the major risk factors for coronary heart disease: smoking, high cholesterol levels, hypertension (persistent high blood pressure), diabetes and abnormal blood sugar levels, and obesity. A person can change or eliminate those risk factors and thus lower their risk of developing or aggravating their heart disease and heart failure.

Among prominent risk factors, hypertension (high blood pressure) and diabetes are particularly important. Uncontrolled high blood pressure increases the risk of heart failure by 200 per cent, compared with those who do not have hypertension. Moreover, the degree of risk appears directly related to the severity of the high blood pressure.

Persons with diabetes have about a two- to eightfold greater risk of heart failure than those without diabetes. Women with diabetes have a greater risk of heart failure than men with diabetes. Part of the risk comes from diabetes' association with other heart failure risk factors, such as high blood pressure, obesity, and high cholesterol levels. However, the disease process in diabetes also damages the heart muscle.

The presence of coronary disease is among the greatest risks for heart failure. Muscle damage and scarring caused by a heart attack greatly increase the risk of heart failure. Cardiac arrhythmias, or irregular heartbeats, also raise heart failure risk. Any disorder that causes abnormal swelling or thickening of the heart sets the stage for heart failure.

In some people, heart failure arises from problems with heart valves, the flap-like structures that help regulate blood flow through the heart. Infections in the heart are another source of increased risk for heart failure.

A single risk factor may be sufficient to cause heart failure, but a combination of factors dramatically increases the risk. Advanced age adds to the potential impact of any heart failure risk.

Finally, genetic abnormalities contribute to the risk for certain types of heart disease, which in turn may lead to heart failure. However, in most instances, a specific genetic link to heart failure has not been identified.

What are the symptoms?

A number of symptoms are associated with heart failure, but none is specific for the condition. Perhaps the best known symptom is shortness of breath ('dyspnea'). In heart failure, this may result from excess fluid in the lungs. The breathing difficulties may occur at rest or during exercise.

In some cases, congestion may be severe enough to prevent or interrupt sleep.

Fatigue or easy tiring is another common symptom. As the heart's pumping capacity decreases, muscles and other tissues receive less oxygen and nutrition, which are carried in the blood. Without proper 'fuel', the body cannot perform as much work, which translates into fatigue.

Fluid accumulation, or edema, may cause swelling of the feet, ankles, legs, and, occasionally, the abdomen. Excess fluid retained by the body may result in weight gain, which sometimes occurs fairly quickly.

Persistent coughing is another common sign, especially coughing that regularly produces mucus or pink, blood-tinged sputum. Some people develop raspy breathing or wheezing.

Because heart failure usually develops slowly, the symptoms may not appear until the condition has progressed over years. The heart hides the underlying problem by making adjustments that delay – but do not prevent – the eventual loss in pumping capacity. The heart adjusts, or compensates, in three ways to cope with and hide the effects of heart failure:

- Enlargement ('dilatation'), which allows more blood into the heart;
- Thickening of muscle fibres ('hypertrophy') to strengthen the heart muscle, which allows the heart to contract more forcefully and pump more blood; and
- More frequent contraction, which increases circulation.

By making these adjustments, or compensating, the heart can temporarily make up for losses in pumping ability, sometimes for years. However, compensation has its limits. Eventually, the heart cannot offset the lost ability to pump blood, and the signs of heart failure appear.

How do doctors diagnose heart failure?

In many cases, physicians diagnose heart failure during a physical examination. Readily identifiable signs are shortness of breath, fatigue, and swollen ankles and feet. The physician also will check for the presence of risk factors, such as hypertension, obesity, and a history of heart problems. Using a stethoscope, the physician can listen to a patient breathe and identify the sounds of lung congestion. The stethoscope also picks up the abnormal heart sounds indicative of heart failure.

If neither the symptoms nor the patient's history point to a clear-cut diagnosis, the physician may recommend any of a variety of laboratory tests, including, initially, an electrocardiogram, which uses recording devices placed on the chest to evaluate the electrical activity of a patient's heartbeat.

Echocardiography is another means of evaluating heart function from outside the body. Sound waves bounced off the heart are recorded and translated into images. The pictures can reveal abnormal heart size, shape, and movement. Echocardiography also can be used to calculate a patient's ejection fraction, a measure of the amount of blood pumped out when the heart contracts.

Another possible test is the chest x-ray, which also determines the heart's size and shape, as well as the presence of congestion in the lungs.

Tests help rule out other possible causes of symptoms. The symptoms of heart failure can result when the heart is made to work too hard, instead of from damaged muscle. Conditions that overload the heart occur rarely and include severe anaemia and thyrotoxicosis (a disease resulting from an overactive thyroid gland).

What treatments are available?

Heart failure caused by an excessive workload is curable by treating the primary disease, such as anaemia or thyrotoxicosis. Also curable are forms caused by anatomical problems, such as a heart valve defect. These defects can be surgically corrected.

However, for the common forms of heart failure – those due to damaged heart muscle – no known cure exists. But treatment for these forms may be quite successful. The treatment seeks to improve patients' quality of life and length of survival through lifestyle change and drug therapy.

Patients can minimise the effects of heart failure by controlling the risk factors for heart disease. Obvious steps include quitting smoking, losing weight if necessary, abstaining from alcohol, and making dietary changes to reduce the amount of salt and fat consumed. Regular, modest exercise is also helpful for many patients, though the amount and intensity should be carefully monitored by a physician.

But, even with lifestyle changes, most heart failure patients must take medication. Many patients receive two or more drugs.

Several types of drugs have proven useful in the treatment of heart failure:

- Diuretics help reduce the amount of fluid in the body and are useful for patients with fluid retention and hypertension.
- Digitalis increases the force of the heart's contractions, helping to improve circulation.
- Results of recent studies have placed more emphasis on the use of drugs known as angiotensin converting enzyme (ACE) inhibitors. Several large studies have indicated that ACE inhibitors improve survival among heart failure patients and may slow, or perhaps even prevent, the loss of heart pumping activity.

Originally developed as a treatment for hypertension, ACE

inhibitors help heart failure patients by, among other things, decreasing the pressure inside blood vessels. As a result, the heart does not have to work as hard to pump blood through the vessels.

Patients who cannot take ACE inhibitors may get a nitrate and/or a drug called hydralazine, each of which helps relax tension in blood vessels to improve blood flow.

Sometimes, heart failure is life-threatening. Usually, this happens when drug therapy and lifestyle changes fail to control its symptoms. In such cases, a heart transplant may be the only treatment option. However, candidates for transplantation often have to wait months or even years before a suitable donor heart is found. Recent studies indicate that some transplant candidates improve during this waiting period through drug treatment and other therapy, and can be removed from the transplant list.

Transplant candidates who do not improve sometimes need mechanical pumps, which are attached to the heart. Called left ventricular assist devices (LVADs), the machines take over part or virtually all of the heart's blood-pumping activity. However, current LVADs are not permanent solutions for heart failure but are considered bridges to transplantation.

An experimental surgical procedure for severe heart failure is available at a few US medical centres. The procedure, called cardiomyoplasty, involves detaching one end of a muscle in the back, wrapping it around the heart, and then suturing the muscle to the heart. An implanted electric stimulator causes the back muscle to contract, pumping blood from the heart.

Can a person live with heart failure?

Heart failure is one of the most serious symptoms of heart disease. About two-thirds of all patients die within 5 years of diagnosis. However, some live beyond 5 years, even into old age. The outlook for an individual patient depends on the patient's age, severity of heart failure, overall health, and a number of other factors.

As heart failure progresses, the effects can become quite severe, and patients often lose the ability to perform even modest physical activity. Eventually, the heart's reduced pumping capacity may interfere with routine functions, and patients may become unable to care for themselves. The loss in functional ability can occur quickly if the heart is further weakened by heart attacks or the worsening of other conditions that affect heart failure, such as diabetes and coronary heart disease.

Heart failure patients also have an increased risk of sudden death, or cardiac arrest, caused by an irregular heartbeat.

To improve the chances of surviving with heart failure, patients must take care of themselves. Patients must:
- See their physician regularly;
- Closely follow all of their physician's instructions;
- Take any medication according to instructions; and
- Immediately inform their physician of any significant change in their condition, such as an intensified shortness of breath or swollen feet.

Patients with heart failure also should:
- Control their weight;
- Watch what they eat;
- Not smoke cigarettes or use other tobacco products; and
- Abstain from or strictly limit alcohol consumption.

Even with the best care, heart failure can worsen, but patients who don't take care of themselves are almost writing themselves a prescription for poor health.

The best defence against heart failure is the prevention of heart disease. Almost all of the major coronary risk factors can be controlled or eliminated: smoking, high cholesterol, high blood pressure, diabetes, and obesity.

What is the outlook for heart failure?

Within the past decade, knowledge of heart failure has improved dramatically but, clearly, much more remains to be learned. The National Heart, Lung, and Blood Institute (NHLBI) supports numerous research projects aimed at building on what is already known about heart failure and at uncovering new knowledge about its process, diagnosis, and treatment. NHLBI research priorities for heart failure include:
- Learning more about basic cellular changes that lead to heart failure;
- Developing tests to detect the earliest signs of heart failure;
- Identifying factors that cause heart failure to worsen;
- Determining how heart failure can be reversed once it starts;
- Understanding better the heart's ability to compensate for lost pumping ability; and
- Developing new therapies, especially those based on early signs of heart failure.

Making the most of your doctor visit

Here are some points you may want to discuss with your doctor. Don't hesitate to ask questions to clarify points. Also, ask your doctor to rephrase a reply you cannot understand. You may want to take a family member or friend to the appointment with you to help you better understand and remember what's said.
- Briefly describe your symptoms, even those you feel may not be important. You may want to keep a list so you will remember them.
- Tell the doctor all of the medications you take – including over-the-counter drugs – and any problems you may be having with them.
- Be sure you understand all of the doctor's instructions – especially for medications. Know what drug to take when, how often, and in what amount.
- Find out what side-effects are possible from any drug the doctor prescribes for you.
- Ask the meaning of any medical term you don't understand.
- If, after your appointment, you still have questions or are uncertain about your treatment, call the doctor's office to get the information you need.
- Information from the National Heart, Lung, and Blood Institute.

How to prevent heart disease

Information from BUPA

What is heart disease and why should I be concerned?

Heart disease is a name given to a variety of conditions that affect the performance of the heart. Important examples of heart disease include:

- angina, in which there is poor blood circulation to the heart,
- heart attack, in which there is death of part of the heart muscle,
- arrhythmia, in which the rate or rhythm of the heart beat is abnormal.

In the UK, heart disease kills more people, both men and women, than any other disease. One British adult dies of heart disease every three minutes.

Your heart is the engine that drives your body. It is a powerful muscle that pumps blood to your entire body, providing the oxygen and nutrients that you need to live. The average human heart works at a rate of 100,000 beats a day or an incredible 2,500 million beats over a lifetime of 70 years.

Your heart is designed to last a lifetime, but you have to do your bit to help ensure it stays in good working order. There are many steps you can take to help prevent heart disease from developing. Read on to find out how you can increase your chances of having and maintaining a healthy, functioning heart.

How important is exercise for a healthy heart?

Exercise is the one of the best – and most enjoyable – ways of lowering your chances of developing heart disease. Regular exercise helps your heart to become stronger, so it can pump more blood around your body with less effort. Indeed, if you exercise on a regular basis, the chance of you developing heart disease is about half that of people who do no exercise at all. Exercise can also help reduce high cholesterol and high blood pressure (both of which can lead to heart disease), help you to sleep better and help provide a feeling of well-being.

People of all ages can benefit from physical activity. Try to exercise at least three to four times a week for about 30 minutes each day. If you have a busy schedule, you can break up those 30 minutes into three 10-minute sessions – it is the total time that you exercise per day that counts. You can choose from a wide range of activities, including brisk walking, cycling, dancing and swimming. We know that even moderate, daily activity, such as gardening, mowing the lawn or taking the stairs instead of the lift, can help your heart. If you have not exercised recently, be sure to check with your doctor before starting any exercise programme.

Should I stop smoking?

Yes. Giving up smoking not only reduces your risk of developing heart disease, but also the risk of many other serious illnesses, like cancer and emphysema. No matter how old you are, it is not too late to stop. As soon as you do, your health will improve immediately. Studies show that, after five years of giving up, the risk of developing heart disease is the same as for someone who has never smoked.

Giving up smoking is not easy and it may take several tries before you succeed.

Keep in mind that plenty of help is available – nicotine patches or gum, acupuncture and hypnotherapy are just a few of your options. Ask your doctor for advice. Also, a number of local and national organisations and helplines can offer you advice.

You can also call QUITline (0800 002 200) free from 9am to 11pm. This is a national helpline that can provide sound advice and information on giving up smoking.

What about high blood pressure?

High blood pressure increases your chances of developing heart disease, but there are usually no signs or

symptoms of high blood pressure, so you may not be aware you have it. That's why you need to have your blood pressure checked by your doctor at least once every five years.

If you have high blood pressure, it can be treated in many ways. Making changes to your lifestyle is a first important step. Try to:
- keep at a healthy weight or lose weight, if necessary,
- reduce the amount of salt you eat,
- give up smoking,
- learn to relax and reduce stress,
- cut down on alcohol if necessary,
- exercise (see above).

If needed, your doctor may prescribe medication to lower your blood pressure. Be sure to follow your doctor's instructions for taking it and discuss any problems or side-effects with him or her.

Why should I cut back on alcohol?

We know that people who drink heavily are more likely to die of heart disease than those who do not. So, if you drink, do so in moderation.

BUPA recommends that a safe limit for men is no more than 3 units of alcohol per day, and for women, no more than 2 units per day. (One unit is equal to half a pint of normal-strength beer or lager, or a single pub measure of spirits, wine or sherry.) Try to leave two alcohol-free days a week and avoid alcohol binges. What is important is alcohol drunk on each day, so if you have drunk no units for a week you cannot assume it is safe to drink 21 units (for men) or 14 units (for women) in a binge.

You may have seen recent reports that drinking in moderation (with an emphasis on moderation) may offer some protection against heart disease. But, if you never drink or seldom drink, do not change your habits – alcohol should not be taken as a medicine.

What about my eating habits?

Eating well can also help prevent heart disease. No one food can provide all the nutrition you need, so eat a variety of foods every day from the following four food groups:
- bread, other cereals and potatoes,
- fruits and vegetables,

- low-fat milk and dairy foods,
- meat, fish and alternatives such as beans and lentils.

Try to cut down on the amount of salt that you add to your food and avoid processed foods that have a high salt content. Choose healthy cooking methods (grill, bake, steam or microwave instead of frying), trim fat off meat and remove skin from chicken. Most importantly, cut down on foods that contain saturated fat, such as pies, sausages and cream. Saturated fat raises the level of cholesterol in your blood. Cholesterol is a white, waxy substance found in all animal tissues. It is essential to life and a vital part of every cell in your body. However, when the level of cholesterol becomes too high, it can lead to blockage of or reduction in the flow of blood through your vessels, and thus to heart disease. Reducing the amount of saturated fat in your diet helps prevent high cholesterol levels.

• The above information is an extract from BUPA's web site which can be found at www.bupa.co.uk
© BUPA/Mosby International 1996-99

Exercise tips

Information from the National Heart Research Fund

There are many ways you can improve the strength of your heart and reduce the risk of heart disease, and you don't need to spend a small fortune achieving it. Here are a few of the simple heart beating measures you can take . . .

No matter how old you are or whatever your level of fitness, exercise can be of immense benefit to your heart. Exercise strengthens all your muscles including your heart and helps boost blood circulation.

You can find exercise opportunities in many daily activities. From gardening, housework and walking the dog to taking the stairs instead of the lift, we can all do more to be active and energetic.

More importantly, you should exercise regularly. One afternoon's strenuous exercise every three weeks

is no good. To feel the benefit, you should aim to build up your exercise routine to at least half an hour every day, following a plan or routine that suits your lifestyle.

The best form of exercise is the

one that you enjoy and that you fit into your daily routine: team games, swimming, walking, taking part in an aerobics class or simply enjoying a brisk walk.

On a practical level, exercise does more for you than you think:
- Reduces the risk of heart attack or stroke
- Can help you lose weight and improve your figure
- It helps you relax and cope with stress
- It gives you energy to do the other things you enjoy
- It helps you to look and feel younger
- It doesn't have to take long, a brisk-paced 20-minute walk as fast as you can, three times a week is all you need.
© National Heart Research Fund

Healthy tips

Information from Heartpoint

Tips to avoid overeating

- Slow down, chew with purpose: take at least 20 minutes to consume a meal. Taking longer to eat will make you feel as though you are eating more. Enjoy the conversation and companionship.
- Eat only while sitting down: much extra food is consumed on the run. Making it a point to sit down while eating will help you think about how much you are consuming.
- Eat off smaller plates!
- Drink a 12-ounce glass of water before eating: it will take up room in your stomach and make you feel less hungry.
- Wait 10 minutes before snacking: between-meal snacks are usually impulsive acts. A wait before eating them will often make you realise you aren't hungry after all.
- Keep the right stuff up front: make such foods as fruit and vegetables readily available by keeping them in the front of the refrigerator shelves.

Low-fat eating

Here are some specific tips on eating a low-fat diet. Remember it's not as hard as it seems.

- Make a shopping list.
- Eat more vegetables, fruit and grains.
- You don't have to stop eating foods you enjoy that are high in fat, just cut down on the amount of their servings. Use bigger quantities of low-fat foods to accompany them.
- Instead of a steak that covers the whole plate, get a cut that you really like of modest size. 4 ounces of beef is recommended – that's a steak about the size of a deck of cards.
- Flavour your stew with meat in modest amounts, don't overpower it.
- Eat one egg instead of two.

- Eat fatty foods less often. You don't have to quit your favourite foods completely. For example, you don't have to have meat every day.
- Trim the visible fat. Remove all of the skin from poultry.
- Limit organ meats (liver, kidney).
- Use lunch meats sparingly (salami, bologna, sausage).
- Make egg dishes with egg whites rather than egg yolks.
- Drink skimmed or 1% milk (if you drink milk).
- Watch the cheese (sorry!). Look for low-fat varieties, especially for cooking.
- Don't add fat as you cook. Instead of frying, use these techniques :
  – Roasting (on a rack if possible so fat drains away)
  – Grilling
  – Baking.
- Don't settle for dull. A little imagination can go a long way in keeping foods interesting:
  – Try new spices
  – Get a good low-fat cookbook with a number of recipes and alternatives. Invest a little time in planning some good alternatives.
- Cut down on added fats, such as salad dressing and butter. Try and use those which are low in saturated fats, and in moderation!
- Avoid: butter, lard, palm oil, coconut oil. (These contain about 40% saturated fat.)
- Use: olive oil. Use a vegetable oil spray to brown or sauté food. Canola, safflower, sunflower, peanut, and corn oil. (These contain about 20% saturated fat.)
- Read the labels. Unfortunately, you really have to pay attention to some foods that say 'Healthy' or 'No cholesterol'. They may still contain large amounts of fat and saturated fat!
- Make some reasonable substitutions.
- Use prudence when dining out.
- Keep on trying ! !

Tips for eating out

Many patients have found themselves very capable of eating properly at home but quickly fall into old habits when it's time to eat out. During the past 10 years or so, however, restaurants have become more aware that many of their patrons are on restricted diets. There is absolutely no reason to feel uncomfortable about ordering

a baked potato and a salad in a fine restaurant. In fact, you can and should make special requests for foods that are more appropriate to your needs. Keep the following tips in mind when you order a meal:

- Entrées covered with sauces, as well as creamy dressing, thick soups and casseroles should be avoided because they are usually rich in fat.
- Order a low-fat appetiser and a salad. Specify that it come with your partner's entrée.
- Avoid fried foods. Choose baked, broiled, boiled, roasted, steamed and grilled.
- Club soda, herbal tea, and decaffeinated coffee are good choices of beverages at a meal, as is a glass of ice water with a wedge of lemon or lime.
- Sourdough, wholewheat, rye and French breads are lower in saturated fats than biscuits, white bread, and dinner rolls.
- Salads are available almost everywhere. Order salads with reduced-calorie salad dressing. Choosing your meal from the salad bar is a good source of good foods (omitting the occasional fat-laden salads and salad dressings that are sometimes there!).
- Ask to have sauces and gravies omitted, or 'on the side'.
- Look for items labelled 'heart-healthy' on the menu.
- Don't be afraid to ask how a dish is prepared.
- Substitute low-fat choices (steamed vegetables for creamed sauces, baked potatoes for french fries, etc.).
- Avoid items described with terms like battered, creamed, au gratin, scalloped, breaded. Good terms include au jus, poached, steamed, baked, etc.
- Pizza: choose thin-crust, avoid meat toppings and get small amounts of cheese (if you pat the top of a pizza with a napkin, this will soak up a lot of extra fat).
- Pastas: good choices if accompanied by red marinara sauce or simple vegetables. Avoid cream or meat sauces.
- Sandwiches: choose lean and not processed meat, get extra lettuce and tomato, and hold the mayo.
- Dessert: order the fresh fruit. If you HAVE to have that chocolate decadence (or whatever your hot button is), split it with a companion, and make sure you cut down somewhere else. Okay, I'm feeling sorry for you, sometimes you simply cannot resist temptation . . . eat the whole thing, but feel very guilty (and make sure you cut down somewhere else).

The most important things to do

While we fret about the most complex and controversial aspects of our health care, don't forget to do these basic things that will definitely help your health. You don't need to go to medical school to be the most important member of your healthcare team – just follow these time-tested ways that really work.

Stop smoking
There is no question that if you smoke, stopping will be the very best thing you will ever do for your health. If you fail this time, keep on trying!

Get some exercise
Even a little is very helpful. You don't have to be an Olympic athlete to gain the benefits of exercise, which can occur at surprisingly low levels. Take a 15-minute walk . . . take the stairs . . . it will do a lot of good.

Eat sensibly
If you can't be perfect, do as well as you can. Don't just give up on good eating habits because it seems too hard.

Learn to take your own blood pressure
Write it down. Bring the list to your doctor. This is the best way to avoid too much or too little treatment for this controllable disease.

If you're overweight, trim a little off
At least don't gain weight. Weight loss is hard because it's a lifetime attitude that will accomplish the goal, but the benefits to your health and how well you feel are definitely worth it.

Work on balance
Be involved . . . without being overly stressed . . . and leave time for relaxation. This is a big challenge for all of us, but it's really important for people with medical conditions, particularly those involving the heart.

Take an aspirin a day
As long as your physician has not told you to avoid it. It is an easy and inexpensive way to prevent heart attacks and strokes, particularly for middle-aged males.

Find a doctor you like
Don't just take what comes along. Your health care depends most on you, but it's your job to find physicians who you can relate to, understand and trust.

Get and maintain health insurance
Let's be realistic – this is an increasingly important part of your health care. Always be careful to maintain it.

Be sceptical about information sources
There is a lot of incomplete, inaccurate, or simply wrong information available. This may be from relatives, acquaintances, charlatans, or the news media.

If you're a woman past your menopause, consider replcement hormones
The issues are a bit complex, but hormones can keep your arteries and heart young, and your bones strong.

If you have a question, ask!
There are really no stupid questions. None of us were born knowing the answers. Ask, and you can put your mind at ease and do the right things for your health.

Continue to be positive. You can 'beat' these diseases
The advances in medicine, and heart disease in particular, have truly been staggering. Applying what we already know to your health care can lead to continued good health . . . and just wait until the next developments!

© 1999 HeartPoint

Keep your heart healthy

Information from BUPA

Heart disease is a major cause of disability in the UK, and it is thought to be the single biggest cause of death in men and women. We know more about heart disease than ever before and there are many ways you can help to protect yourself. The most common type of heart disease is coronary artery disease (CAD) and this will be the focus of these pages, along with information about your blood pressure and cholesterol level.

Coronary artery disease (CAD)

It is estimated that one in every four men will have a heart attack before the age of 65, and CAD seems to be on the increase in women. The lifestyles we choose, the way our bodies work and our family medical history all play an important part in our chance of having CAD.

What is coronary artery disease?

The heart is a powerful muscular pump, and the action of the heart muscle depends on its own supply of blood from the coronary arteries (which provide essential oxygen to the heart muscle).

At birth, the lining of these arteries is smooth, but a disease process called atheroma (from the Ancient Greek *athere* which means 'gruel') leads to the development of the symptoms of CAD – angina or myocardial infarction (heart attack).

Atheroma takes the form of fatty streaks on the lining of the coronary arteries, which gradually enlarge to meet its oxygen needs.

As atheroma builds up, the coronary arteries become narrowed, and sometimes completely blocked, and cannot supply the heart muscle with enough blood to meet its oxygen needs. When a person exerts themselves physically under these circumstances, the heart muscle demands more blood and oxygen than is available from the blood supply. This produces pain in the chest – the classic symptom of angina. There are now effective treatments for angina such as nitrates which dilate the coronary arteries; beta blockers, which reduce heart rate and blood pressure, and calcium antagonists which reduce blood pressure. All these drugs either improve oxygen supply to the heart, or lower the heart's demand for oxygen.

A heart attack is caused when the atheroma ruptures and releases fat into the channel of the coronary artery. This can result in the blood clotting and completely blocking the blood supply to one part of the heart muscle. This causes severe chest pain and is an emergency situation which requires urgent admission to hospital.

What causes CAD – risk factors and how to reduce them

There has been an immense amount of research into CAD, and, with so much known about the causes of it, the good news is that you can significantly reduce your risk of developing it. And, if you already have CAD, it is possible to reduce your risk of a heart attack in the future.

- Smoking increases your risk of developing CAD. The greater the number of cigarettes smoked and the more years you have smoked – the greater your risk of developing CAD.
- Diet is a major feature in CAD. Eating too many foods rich in saturated fats, too few foods high in unsaturated fats and not enough fresh vegetables and fruit can increase your risk of developing coronary artery disease.
- Physical exercise keeps your heart, mind and body healthy.
- Stress is a slightly more difficult topic to assess, but it's widely believed that too much stress in your life, whether at work, at home or in your personal relationships may increase your risk of developing coronary heart disease.
- Blood just seems to go about its business without much ado, and we rarely think of its influence on our health. But normal blood pressure, cholesterol and glucose are all essential to the working of our bodies.
- Family history of early (before the age of 55 years in male relatives and 65 in female)

coronary heart disease in a blood relative, for example a parent, brother or sister, increases your own risk of developing the disease. This is most probably due to your genetic inheritance, but may also be due to the social environment of your family – where certain lifestyles can predispose to coronary heart disease.

- Hormones, or early menopause (before age 45 years), whether occurring naturally or due to removal of the ovaries, are both associated with an increased risk of coronary heart disease. This increased risk may be reduced by hormone replacement therapy (HRT).

Help keep your blood pressure down!

The heart is a powerful muscle which – like the other muscles in your body – contracts. When this happens, a surge of pressure is exerted on the blood vessels which lead from the heart to the rest of the body. The peak pressure as the heart contracts is called the systolic blood pressure, and the lower pressure when the heart relaxes is called the diastolic blood pressure. A typical pressure in a young man might be 120/80 mmHg (mmHg = millimetres of mercury).

High blood pressure is a risk factor for strokes and heart attacks. A 10mm rise in diastolic blood pressure is associated with an approximate doubling of the risk of stroke and a 50 per cent increase in the risk of a heart attack. If the risk of a heart attack or stroke is very low as in young people, without other risk factors such as high cholesterol or regular smoking, borderline blood pressure elevation does not pose a significant threat.

However, as individuals become older, or when these other risk factors are significant, slightly elevated blood pressure can present a greater risk. Before any treatment for high blood pressure is prescribed, a complete assessment of health is required, including repeated blood pressure measurements.

What is normal blood pressure?
There is no single normal blood pressure average for healthy individuals, since blood pressure changes with age. The average blood pressure in a man of 50, for example, is 133/83 mmHg, whilst in a man of 70, the average value is 147/81 mmHg. There is a wide spread of values on each side of these averages and figures higher than this are not necessarily of any medical significance.

Measuring blood pressure
The conventional method for measuring blood pressure still requires inflation of a cuff applied to the upper arm, then listening for sounds in the artery below the cuff with a stethoscope, while the applied pressure is measured on a manometer. This test is usually carried out by a doctor or nurse. However there are many devices you can buy over the counter which allow you to measure your own blood pressure. The accuracy of some of these devices is open to question, as your blood pressure can vary quite dramatically. If you measure it yourself and get a high result, you should always go and have it checked by your GP.

Newer techniques enable blood pressure to be measured repeatedly using an automatic device which codes results on tape and can subsequently be decoded to provide a 24-hour blood pressure profile. These 24-hour monitoring devices are increasingly used to detect those people who have high blood pressure when measured by a doctor, but normal blood pressure at all other times.

Keeping the pressure down . . .
Blood pressure, like your height and weight, is a characteristic of you. It is the product of several different factors: inheritance is very important

---

Eating too many foods rich in saturated fats, too few foods high in unsaturated fats and not enough fresh vegetables and fruit can increase your risk of developing CAD

---

and people who have high blood pressure often have a parent, brother or sister who has also suffered from elevated blood pressure – although this may not always be known to the person. Diet, stress and exercise also affect blood pressure. Stress is difficult to assess, but anything that makes excessive demands on you – especially work – seems to be associated with high blood pressure.

Salt intake has also received a lot of publicity. There is now strong evidence that restricting salt will cause a reduction of blood pressure in some (but by no means all) people with high blood pressure. Reducing your salt intake is fairly easy – don't add salt to your food either on the plate or during cooking, avoid heavily salted foods such as processed meats, some breakfast cereals, mayonnaise, salted butter and cheese. Even bread in substantial quantities increases salt intake significantly.

Keep a check on your cholesterol

Cholesterol receives a huge amount of coverage, but some of the messages can seem very confusing. Is cholesterol good or bad? Should it be high or low?

What is cholesterol?
Cholesterol is a fatty substance present in all human cells. A certain amount of cholesterol in the blood is necessary for good health – almost all of this is made in the liver, the remainder is absorbed from the diet, mainly from meat and dairy products, and egg yolks.

The good and the bad . . .
Because cholesterol is a fatty substance, it must be packaged for transportation in the blood. These 'packages' are called lipoproteins which contain protein and fat, as well as cholesterol. There are several types of lipoproteins, but two of them seem to carry the most significance, especially in terms of heart disease. LDL (low density lipoprotein) is bad cholesterol – you do not want to have large quantities of it in your blood. HDL (high density lipoprotein) is good. A third group of fats, triglycerides, may also be a risk factor for heart disease.

The bad cholesterol

LDL is the 'bad cholesterol'. LDL is mostly made of fat with a small amount of protein. LDL carries cholesterol from the liver to other parts of the body where it is needed for cell repair and other activities. However, LDL can build up on the walls of the arteries and over a period of time, this build-up of cholesterol causes the arteries to harden and narrow. This causes reduced blood flow to the body's tissues and the heart muscle (or atherosclerosis).

By lowering LDL, a person can reduce the risk of atherosclerosis, heart attack, and other complications.

The good cholesterol

HDL is 'good cholesterol'. It is mostly made up of protein and a small amount of fat. HDL helps clear cholesterol from the body by scavenging leftover LDL from the bloodstream and carrying it back to the liver for disposal. If you know or think you are a high risk for heart disease, raising your HDL levels may be beneficial for you, as low HDL is thought to increase the risk of coronary artery disease, while high levels of HDL appear to help protect against the disease.

Although high cholesterol (LDL) is an important risk for coronary artery disease and stroke, it is only one of many risk factors that can contribute to these health problems. Other risk factors may be as important or more important than your cholesterol level.

Tests for cholesterol and what the results mean

The test for cholesterol is usually just a simple matter of taking a blood sample from a vein and identifying the levels of HDL and LDL. You don't need to alter your diet or fast before you have the test. How often to have your cholesterol levels measured is best determined by your GP in the light of your family history of heart disease. For most people, once every five years is reasonable.

Cholesterol is measured in millimoles per litre. An ideal total cholesterol level is less than 5.2mmol/l.

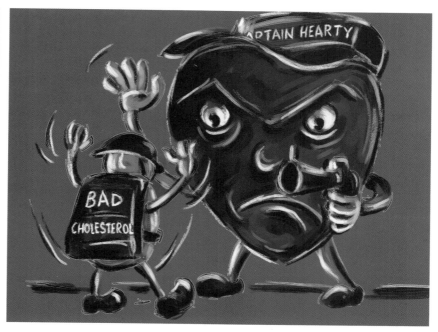

How to lower LDLs and raise HDLs

Watch your cholesterol intake carefully. All the cholesterol you require is produced by your body – anything else you eat is surplus to the amount required by your body. It's not that difficult!

Lower LDL in your blood by:
- cutting down on animal fats, especially eggs, full-fat cheese and milk, ice cream, butter
- increasing your fibre intake (eat more bran, brown rice, leafy greens)
- increasing your intake of complex carbohydrates (such as rice, pulses)
- trying to lose a little weight if you are overweight

Raise HDL in your blood by:
- upping your exercise regime, at least three periods of 20 minutes each of vigorous exercise a week
- stopping smoking
- trying to lose weight if you are overweight
- and, remarkably, moderate consumption of red wine can also increase HDL cholesterol, but never use alcohol as a medication – the benefits must be balanced against the increased risk of alcoholism, cirrhosis of the liver and traffic accidents, and breast cancer in women

What is Benecol?

'Benecol' is the name of a range of foods which may be able to reduce cholesterol in certain people. It has been widely available in Finland for around three years, and is now on supermarket shelves in the UK (around £2.50 for a tub of the margarine).

The Benecol range includes margarine and cheese spreads. The margarine is rich in plant stanol ester, a substance which may lower cholesterol in some people by up to 10 per cent. It does this by preventing cholesterol being absorbed during the digestive process (remember that most cholesterol is produced by the body – and Benecol will not affect this). It is probably most beneficial for adults who have moderately raised cholesterol.

Please note: If you are already taking drugs to reduce your cholesterol level, do continue to take them – Benecol should not be used to replace them. Benecol is not suitable for children or pregnant women. If you are at all unsure, always seek the advice of your GP.

A final word

Studies show that it is possible to slow, even reverse, the build-up of fatty deposits in artery walls. Saying it's too late is rubbish! You can reduce your risk of CAD by making dietary and lifestyle changes.

• The above information is an extract from the BUPA web site, which can be found on www.bupa.co.uk
© BUPA 1996-99

Public to operate heart machines

By Michael White,
Political Editor

The Government will today announce plans to set up a chain of defibrillators in public places like airports, shopping malls and railway stations to help to reduce the incidence of heart attacks which kill people before an ambulance arrives.

In a number of pilot projects, designated volunteers who work in the neighbourhood will be trained to use the equipment.

The idea is to prevent potentially fatal coronary damage immediately after heart attacks as ambulance paramedics now do with growing success.

What ministers have dubbed Britain's 'clot-busters' scheme will be part of Frank Dobson's long-promised white paper on public health, which aims to pioneer new methods of curbing killer diseases and targets everything from diet and fluoride in water to poor mental health.

But the health secretary is an avowed populist who is keen to avoid charges of being a 'food fascist' and to focus attention on the poorest social groups, whose health risks are usually well above average.

'We want to take public health of the think-tank and the nanny state into the realm of the real world, to benefit real people,' one Dobson aide said last night.

In a further eye-catching gesture Mr Dobson, whose final draft has been the subject of protracted tussles between Tessa Jowell, the public health minister, and the more cautious officials at the Downing Street policy unit, will also unveil the NHS equivalent of local 'meteorological offices' for health.

> **The Government will set up a chain of defibrillators in public places like airports, shopping malls and railway stations**

'They're meant to be like the long-range weather forecast,' aides said.

By linking local public health offices with universities and local authorities, Mr Dobson hopes they will be better placed to predict both short-term health problems, a looming winter epidemic, and more deeply rooted ones like persistent cancer patterns or high incidence of heart disease such as are suffered in west Scotland.

With Tony Blair anxious to signal to Labour's wavering 'core voters' that his team is delivering on their agenda, the health secretary will also claim success today for one of his earlier initiatives: the chain of NHS Direct telephone helplines, staffed by nurses.

It has taken 250,000 calls and eased the pressure on hard-pressed GPs and hospital emergency rooms, Mr Dobson will tell MPs.

That claim will coincide with unrest over NHS Direct and other government policies at this week's annual conference of the British Medical Association in Belfast.

Mr Dobson will remind doctors not only that the scheme eases their burdens, but that it occasionally corrects misdiagnosis by GPs, including heart attacks dismissed as indigestion.

In one case an NHS Direct nurse talked a would-be suicide off a rail bridge at Paddington station, London. She could hear the trains in the background.

© The Guardian
July, 1999

STAND CLEAR — WHILE WE KICK START LOCAL PUBLIC HEALTH!!

Exercise and your heart

Information from the Coronary Prevention Group

There's no doubt about it. Leading an active life makes you fit for life. Years of evidence have accumulated to show what many people already know – exercise makes you feel better and look better. The opposite is also true. Studies show that lack of exercise contributes to the nation's number one killer: coronary heart disease. People who don't take adequate exercise regularly are twice as likely to have a heart attack as those who do.

But don't panic, this doesn't mean that everyone has to rush into competitive sport. Exercise isn't just sport. For a healthy heart, exercise means regular, moderate to vigorous, physical activity of the right kind, and this information will show that it's easier than you think to fit into your daily life.

Your heart is a muscle

In many ways your heart is a muscle just like any other. If you don't exercise it regularly it gets weak. Those of you who've seen what a limb looks like after it's been in plaster for weeks will know how bad a 'wasted' muscle looks. In some ways, life in modern Britain is like encasing your whole body in plaster!

Our daily routines often involve nothing more active than standing or sitting for long periods of the day. This is not at all what a human body was designed for and it leaves our muscles, including our heart, less efficient than they should be.

Even at rest the heart has to pump five litres of blood round your body every minute. An unfit heart has to work harder to do this. Additional, quite ordinary tasks, like walking to work or carrying the shopping, are quite tiring if you are unfit and more exertion (such as running for the bus) becomes a real strain.

When you exert yourself, your muscles need more oxygen than usual so your heart has to beat faster to take more oxygen (which is carried in the blood) to your muscles. But if you exercise regularly your muscles use oxygen more efficiently, your heart pumps more blood with each beat and it doesn't have to beat as fast. Even when you are resting, a strong heart needs fewer beats to circulate blood round your system. Daily routines and chores are much less tiring with a trained and efficient heart and of course strenuous activities can be undertaken with much less effort and for longer periods. In other words, vigorous activity increases your stamina.

Many types of exercise are good for suppleness and strength and those are important for general health and fitness, especially as you get older. But it's activities which improve stamina that are best for your heart and there are plenty of examples of these in this information.

Exercise and cholesterol

The higher the level of cholesterol in your blood the higher the risk of developing coronary heart disease. Eating too much fat, particularly saturated fat, encourages your body to make too much cholesterol. If there is too much cholesterol in your blood it tends to 'fur up' your arteries, slowing down the blood supply to your heart. So it's good idea to watch your diet. The Coronary Prevention Group (CPG) has a booklet on blood cholesterol which gives you more details.

But eating healthily isn't the only way to affect blood cholesterol levels. Exercise is also important. Regular, vigorous physical activity lowers the total amount of cholesterol in your blood to a worthwhile degree. It can also change the composition of blood cholesterol – increasing the amount of 'good' cholesterol (known as high density lipoprotein or HDL) and reducing the amount of 'bad' cholesterol (low density lipoprotein or LDL and triglycerides, another type of blood fat).

Exercise and blood pressure

Along with smoking and raised blood cholesterol levels, high blood pressure is one of the main risk factors for coronary heart disease. High blood pressure can damage your arteries and put a strain on your heart. But like raised blood cholesterol levels, this can be reduced. Study after study has shown that regular, moderate to vigorous exercise can help prevent your blood pressure going up as you get older and can also help to bring it down in people in mild hypertension (high blood pressure). CPG's booklet *Blood Pressure and Your Heart* explains how blood pressure works.

Exercise and weight control

Being overweight is another risk factor in the development of coronary heart disease. There are no miracle short-cuts to losing weight permanently. But exercise can help you lose weight – and keep it under control.

The rate at which you use the energy (calories) in your food is called your metabolic rate. Exercise can increase your metabolic rate, not only while you were exercising but also, it seems, after you've finished the session. This is especially important for people trying to lose weight because the body can react to a reduced energy (calorie) intake by slowing down the metabolic rate – using up less energy (calories) than before.

Regular physical activity keeps the metabolism ticking along nice and vigorously, so that eventually you can go back to eating your full quota of healthy food. Provided you keep up with the exercise, you could enjoy a truly 'hearty' appetite!

An added bonus to losing the weight by combining a diet with exercise is that you can often improve body shape and posture. While exercise 'burns off' fat, it puts on muscle and since muscle is firmer and stronger than flab, body tone improves, and with it posture.

Remember, too, that the muscle is heavier than fat, so if you lose 4lbs in weight you may actually have lost 8lbs of fat!

Exercise to relax?

People often think that stress is one of the main causes of heart attacks. But experts can't agree on how important stress is in relation to coronary heart disease. Even so, most would say that stress adds to the risk and is best reduced if possible. CPG's booklet *Stress and Your Heart* gives some advice on how to avoid stress and its effects.

Although there hasn't been nearly as much research on the psychological benefits of exercise as on the physical benefits, the evidence does show that exercise can lift depression, reduce anxiety, help you sleep better and generally bolster your self-esteem. And the best part is that some benefits are immediate. The physical benefits of exercise may take a little while to materialise but you can feel better straight away!

So to sum up so far: exercise makes your heart healthy and more efficient, increases the 'good' and decreases the 'bad' cholesterol in your bloodstream, helps to keep your blood pressure down and control your weight, and makes you feel good! Some people also find that it helps them to stay off the cigarettes.

Before you start

You're now convinced (we hope!) that an active life is for you. But before you leap off the sofa, there are a few golden rules.

First, start gently and build up your levels of activity gradually. The more unfit you are, the more gradually you should start, but the sooner you'll feel the benefit. The important thing is to be a bit more energetic than you usually are. And don't forget to wear comfortable clothes and shoes – how you feel is more important than how you look.

Second, if it hurts while you're exercising or you feel dizzy or unusually tired – stop. Forget about the macho 'no pain, no gain' stuff. It is wrong and it may be unsafe. Go back to gentler exercise for a while. If it still hurts anywhere, go and see your doctor and check out the

cause. In fact, speaking to your doctor before you start to exercise is recommended if any of the follow-ing apply to you:

- you have high blood pressure (or you haven't checked your blood pressure for more than five years and you haven't a clue what it is. Your GP will be pleased to see you!)
- you have chest pains or chest trouble like asthma or bronchitis
- you have back trouble or pain in other joints, like arthritis
- you have diabetes
- you have a cold or virus
- you're recovering from an illness or an operation
- you're worried about any other aspect of your health.

Having any of these conditions doesn't mean that you won't be able to get active. In fact your doctor may be able to suggest appropriate types of activities which could have particular benefits for you. Even if you have had a heart attack or heart surgery, you could benefit from exercise, as we explain later.

How much is enough?

Now for the nitty gritty: how often do you need to be active, how much activity is enough and how long do you need to keep going to get the benefits? Experts are generally agreed that whatever activity you choose, you should build up to:
Frequency: 2 or 3 times a week +
Intensity: enough to get you slightly breathless +

Time: 20 to 30 minutes per session = FIT! This adds up to just 1% of your time!

Frequency

The important rule here is regularity. Evidence seems to show that 2 or 3 sessions each week are necessary for heart-health but don't panic. One longer session per week is better than nothing and can burn up a lot of energy (calories). If you're really keen you can obviously exercise more frequently.

Intensity

This is the most important part of the exercise equation as far as coronary heart disease is concerned. To make your heart more efficient, activities should be 'aerobic'. Aerobic means 'with oxygen' (not 'with leotard'!) and involves the large muscles contracting and relaxing at a steady, rhythmic pace over a period of time. This allows the heart and lungs to carry enough oxygen to the muscles without too many problems. The idea is to get the heart beating faster than normal by increasing the amount of exercise gradually.

The easy way to test if your chosen activity is aerobic enough for you or not is to exercise to the point where you are slightly breathless but can still carry on a conversation (with yourself if you're on your own!). Don't overdo it by exercising until you are out of breath. It just isn't necessary.

The opposite to aerobic exercise is 'anaerobic' activity. This is exercise 'without oxygen' because the heart and the lungs just can't supply it as fast as your body is using it. Sprinting, weightlifting and press-ups for example are anaerobic as they need short bursts of power. Once you're fit, these activities will build up strength, but they are not a good way to improve your stamina and your heart-health.

Time

The duration? If you're keen on a particular activity, don't restrict yourself to 20 or 30-minute sessions three times a week. It's just that the effect on your heart doesn't improve much after this length of time. So carry on longer if you're feeling fine (and having fun!) but don't push yourself into an endurance test.

If it suits your lifestyle better, do 10 minutes or so of more vigorous activity 7 days a week or about 15 minutes 4 times a week. You don't have to run your life with a stopwatch to get fit and some activity is better than none at all.

Getting started . . .

An exercise test might be just the thing to get you motivated, but it certainly isn't essential and the information you get isn't always as good as it might be. So don't spend a lot of money on one. If it's provided free, perhaps by your employer or as part of a health fair, it's worth a go and the best fitness tests also give plenty of good advice on diet and smoking, as well as exercise.

Another spur to action might be the knowledge that, as well as being good for your heart, exercise has all sorts of benefits we haven't mentioned so far. For example, exercise can keep your bones stronger for longer. As we grow older we tend to lose calcium and this makes your bones weaker. This is most marked in women after the menopause and it is why so many elderly women break their hips if they fall. The right kind of exercise (walking is particularly good) slows down the process.

. . . Keeping going

Once you've started, it's a good idea to set a regular time for your chosen activity so it becomes a habit. If you need or prefer to exercise alone, set yourself goals (e.g. three times around the block today, use the stairs instead of the lift on Monday, Wednesday and Friday) so you can get the feeling of making progress.

You might like to exercise with friends, so you can encourage each other as you make progress (you could even help each other out with transport or baby-sitting arrangements). You could find that exercise is not only a good way to stay in touch with friends but also a way of making new ones.

If you find a good teacher for a particular kind of activity this can be an enormous help. And keep in mind all the ways that exercise helps your heart.
• The above is an extract from www.healthnet.org.uk/healthy/fitrunn.htm

The price of a better — and longer — life

By Sarah Boseley

Life after a heart transplant is much better for most: the defective heart is no longer labouring, they are no longer struggling for breath and some even go on to run the marathon.

The price to be paid is constant medication. To prevent the body rejecting the new heart, the patient's immune system must be suppressed by powerful drugs. Then more drugs are needed, to prevent the side effects of those drugs and to ward off infection.

An average transplant patient at Papworth Hospital in Cambridge, which has done more than 800 heart operations, is on eight to 12 drugs every day, taken two to three times a day.

There are drugs for gastric problems, which are quite common, and large doses of antibiotics in the first three months to stave off infection. They are then used to kill off any slight cough or cold that the immunosuppressed body would not be able to cope with alone. Other drugs will depend on the way the individual patient's body reacts to the transplant.

Among the side-effects of the immunosuppressant drugs can be the growth of body hair. The gums tend to overgrow, causing dental hygiene problems.

There are also dietary changes to be observed, such as not eating live yoghurts – the bacteria that reinforce most people's stomach flora can cause trouble in these patients.

Papworth patients are looked after for the rest of their life, which for half of them will be 10 years. There are few survivors over 20 years, and few patients can endure a second heart transplant.

Medical check-ups are intensive in the first months. The patient stays in hospital for two to three weeks, and has three check-ups in the following week. After that it lessens to every two months, then every three months, and by six months they are generally stable. In the long term, check-ups are every nine months or even annually.

The visit is fairly routine, involving work on an exercise bicycle to measure the heart's performance, and the slight discomfort of a biopsy of the cardiac muscle, which for most transplant patients is nothing compared with what they have previously endured.

The 500 'who fail to survive waiting list for heart surgery'

Too many bypass patients are dying needlessly, warns specialist

By Jenny Hope, Medical Correspondent

Up to five hundred NHS patients die each year while waiting for heart bypass surgery, a leading surgeon claimed yesterday.

Heart specialist Ben Bridgewater said many could be saved if they were given an operation as soon as they were diagnosed.

He added that he believed the Government must increase the priority of heart surgery.

Mr Bridgewater, who works at Wythenshawe Hospital, Manchester, made the estimate of the number of waiting list deaths in the latest edition of the medical journal *Heart* published today.

Around 24,000 people underwent coronary artery bypass surgery in 1996-97 in the UK but research suggests more than two per cent of patients die before they reach the operating theatre.

Under the NHS Patient's Charter the wait for an operation should not be longer than 18 months and in some areas it has reached the limit.

But a study in the Netherlands shows that some patients put on a waiting list will die within a month at home without any warning signs.

Other research shows the chances of a heart patient dying are now twice as high while on a waiting list for NHS treatment than for those risking the complications of surgery.

Success rates for heart surgery are high, with around 95 per cent of patients having their symptoms cured or substantially improved.

Moreover, 20 per cent of patients on the waiting list get admitted for urgent treatment or as emergency cases before their surgery date because their condition has deteriorated. As a result they may be less able to cope with the operation.

Mr Bridgewater said studies in the Netherlands and New Zealand suggest it is almost impossible to spot in advance patients who will not survive time on the waiting list.

He said: 'The Dutch study suggests that to decrease waiting list mortality significantly would require a system whereby surgery was undertaken almost immediately, which currently happens in the UK in the private sector but will not happen in the NHS without an enormous injection of resources.'

At Mr Bridgewater's hospital the average waiting time for a bypass is six months, but the situation has worsened recently.

'If someone comes in today, they will probably have to wait 18 months because we have a lot of urgent cases coming in. I feel terrible, simply awful about the anxiety and worry they are going through,' he said.

A major effort would clear the backlog but it would need extra resources, he said. 'Breast cancer patients were given a two-week guarantee of medical attention and I would like to see that happen in heart surgery.

'In the US heart patients wait a few weeks, Canada a little longer and the situation varies in Europe but the wait is directly related to the amount spent on health – the more spent, the shorter the wait.'

Dr Duncan Dymond, consultant cardiologist at St Bartholomew's Hospital, London, said all heart specialists were aware patients could die on the waiting list.

'Patients ask me what the risks are of having surgery, but I have to say to them the risks of doing nothing are far higher.

'But the problems are in so many areas, not enough doctors, nurses, operating theatre time, intensive care beds, that it needs a strategic change and more resources to bring a major improvement. The good thing about this kind of information being made available is we can no longer expect to put patients on waiting lists without them asking "Is it all right to wait months for my operation?" They know about rationing now.'

© *The Daily Mail*
June, 1999

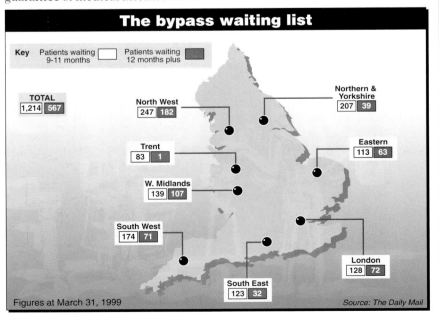

Red wine no protection as French climb the heart disease league

By Sarah Boseley,
Health Correspondent

The myth that drinking red wine protects the French against heart disease has been exploded by scientists who say it is only a matter of time before levels of the illness are the same on both sides of the Channel.

Heart disease rates are much lower in France than in Britain: the death rate is about a quarter of that in the UK

But neither red wine nor the other traditional staples of the Gallic diet have much to do with it, say the scientists.

'The suggestion that consumption of garlic and onions could account for the low mortality from heart disease in France is based on ecological associations and direct supportive evidence is lacking,' says a paper in today's *British Medical Journal*.

The authors, Malcolm Law and Nicholas Wald from the Wolfson institute of preventive medicine, have put forward a 'time lag' hypothesis to explain what is known as 'the French paradox': low rates of heart disease in spite of enthusiastic cheese and meat eating and a lifestyle no more healthy than that enjoyed by the British.

They claim that in France and in other countries such as Italy and Spain, with low ischaemic heart disease levels, animal fat consumption used to be lower than in the UK, but increased to that of Britain between 1970 and 1980.

Examining past and present French heart disease statistics, Dr Law and Professor Wald conclude that it can take 25 years for an increase in a nation's fat consumption to be reflected in heart disease figures.

France and Britain will before long have the same levels of heart disease, they say, although efforts to encourage better diets, less smoking and more exercise could stop levels rising across the Channel.

Wine does have a small preventive effect on heart disease, the scientists acknowledge, but 'drinking more than about one unit a day confers little or no further protection'. Besides, white wine, beer and whisky have exactly the same effect.

And the quantities of wine the French drink cause more problems than they prevent, say the scientists.

'The excess mortality from alcohol-related causes is so large that it abolishes the survival advantage from the low mortality from heart disease, highlighting the public health problem from alcohol in French men.'

French women, however, who drink and smoke much less and eat a good diet, are admirably healthy.

But, commenting on the study in the same edition of the *BMJ*, other scientists wonder whether Dr Law and Prof Wald have the whole story. Meir Stampfer, a Harvard medical school professor and Eric Rimm from the Harvard school of public health, suggest the French habit of drinking with meals may be helpful.

The French diet has other differences from that of the UK and US, they say. What about the Mediterranean staples of rich, dark green leafy vegetables containing folic acid, cereal fibre, nuts and polyunsaturated oils? they ask.

The World Health Organisation and the Food and Agricultural Organisation 'suggest that per capita intake of nuts and fibre has been two to three times higher in France than the UK since 1965'.

Other commentators suggest the French have avoided heart disease through focusing on girls' nutrition, which results in healthier babies.

But in a response, Dr Law and Prof Wald point out that their theory holds not only for France but also for the diverse populations of Spain, Italy, Japan and Soweto.

© *The Guardian*
May, 1999

NHS *to target heart disease*

Milburn pledges £50m and 400 new consultants as focus moves off waiting list targets

By Sarah Boseley, Health Correspondent

Alan Milburn, the health secretary, yesterday pledged £50m and more than 400 new consultants to fight Britain's heart disease epidemic, confirming his determination to steer NHS resources towards those areas where they are most badly needed.

The money will pay for an extra 3,000 heart bypass and angioplasty operations – the enlarging of a furred-up artery – over two years, Mr Milburn told a meeting of heart experts. The new operations represent a 10% increase over the present number carried out.

Next week the health secretary will meet cancer specialists, and is expected to set targets for getting every cancer patient to see a consultant within a fortnight of referral by a GP. His third target is mental health.

'Heart disease, together with cancer, is the country's biggest killer,' said Mr Milburn. 'That is why the NHS services that deal with it are one of my personal priorities for modernisation. I want to see more patients getting the early access to heart surgery that they need. By investing extra resources we will be able to get more patients treated.'

Doctors, managers and patient groups applauded signs that the new secretary of state is prepared to look beyond the political albatross of waiting list targets, but were quick to point out that the heart disease money was not new.

Health professionals accept the £50m is new in that it will not be borrowed from any other part of the NHS, but it is part of the £21bn – spread over three years – announced in the comprehensive spending review last year for the health service. Frank Dobson, health secretary at the time, said that the money would be 'ring-fenced so that it delivers exactly what we want'.

Mr Milburn said the money was intended to make 'maximum use of the cardiac capacity that currently exists in the national health service'. This means NHS trusts will be expected to pay for the extra intensive care, pathology and other services needed to enable existing cardiologists and heart surgeons to perform more operations.

Experts said the £50m would not pay for additional consultants. Nigel Edwards, policy director of the NHS Confederation which represents health authorities and trusts, said it would cost £300m-£400m to get the promised extra 330 cardiologists and 80 cardio-thoracic surgeons working.

'The money they are paid is less the issue than the resources they consume,' he said. 'One consultant has a team of junior doctors. It costs £250,000 per intensive care bed and then there is pathology and blood and so on.'

Mr Milburn said the national service framework on heart disease – a country-wide strategy for tackling it from prevention to cure – will be published shortly. Mr Edwards called the £50m 'the first down payment' on the strategy. 'One's supposition is that the costs associated with it will be much higher than this.' It will have to confront the potentially high costs of cholesterol-lowering drugs for those with heart disease, among other treatments.

Doctors' organisations applauded the direction Mr Milburn was giving, while showing scepticism over the numbers. Professor George Alberti, president of the Royal College of Physicians, who was at the meeting, called the money 'a welcome kick-start', but said that in the long term major increases in cardiologists, nurses, theatre staff and technicians would be needed.

Barry Jackson, president of the Royal College of Surgeons, said of the 400 new posts: 'In principle I thoroughly applaud it. This is what we have been pushing for for a long time.' Other areas also badly needed more consultants: general surgery was short of 800 and there were 580 too few in trauma and orthopaedics.

Peter Hawker, chairman of the British Medical Association's consultants' committee, said it was important to make heart disease a priority, but said the 400 additional specialists were already on the training ladder. He urged Mr Milburn to think about making more training places available. *© The Guardian October, 1999*

Healthy lifestyles

Information from the National Heart Research Fund

Heart Research's 'Healthy Lifestyles' campaign aims to help prevent heart disease by giving simple guidelines for a healthier heart.

Research shows that not smoking, eating a healthy and balanced diet and being active reduces the risk of heart disease significantly. So read below, and discover how easy it can be to take care of yourself.

About the heart

Did you realise . . .

The average heart beats about 70 times a minute, that's 100,800 times every single day of your life.

By the age of 15, over 60% of children have experimented with smoking and around 1 in 4 go on to smoke as adults.

The UK's death rate from coronary heart disease is falling, but it is still among the highest in the western world.

Coronary heart disease affects the arteries which supply blood to the heart. It is usually caused by atherosclerosis, or the 'furring up' of the arteries, resulting in heart attack or angina.

'Furring up' of our arteries is caused by fats and other substances collecting and building up on the artery walls, restricting the blood flow or preventing blood flow altogether.

Every day over 800 people in the UK suffer a heart attack and over 500 die due to heart disease.

There are several everyday things we can do to dramatically reduce the risk of heart disease and follow guidelines that are designed to make our hearts fit for life.

Healthy diet tips

It's a fact, we British eat far too many fatty foods that can easily lead to coronary heart disease. And while regular exercise is one of the most important ways of reducing the risk, a healthy diet is just as important. Helping your heart is really a case of using your head, and not taking your food for granted.

Imbalances can easily occur if you eat too many foods high in saturated fats and cholesterol. They quickly encourage atherosclerosis, and that means bad news for your heart. So how can we make sure what we eat is what is right – and isn't dull?

By adopting a healthy, well balanced diet you can feed your body with all it needs and cut out all it doesn't. And a diet rich in goodness can also be rich in taste and variety.

Reduce the total amount of fat

Cut down on fried food including chips and crisps. Look for lean meat and trim off visible fat. Chicken and turkey are good alternatives. Use low fat products whenever possible e.g. semi-skimmed milk, low fat yoghurt and cheese. Beware of hidden fats in biscuits, cakes, pastries, pies and many other manufactured items.

Change the type of fat

Use a margarine labelled high in poly-unsaturates e.g. sunflower, or mono-unsaturates e.g. olive oil, in place of

---

Every day over 800 people in the UK suffer a heart attack and over 500 die due to heart disease

---

butter. Use small amounts of a suitable oil for cooking e.g. sunflower, corn or olive oil. Do not use lard or dripping.

Eat fish twice a week and one of these should be an oily fish e.g. tuna, herring, mackerel, sardine, salmon or trout.

Fruit, vegetables and salads are very good for health. Try to eat 5 portions a day.

Eat plenty of bread, cereals and potatoes, especially the high fibre kinds e.g. wholemeal bread, wholegrain breakfast cereals and jacket potatoes.

Go easy on salt and sugar.

Make gradual changes and introduce new food whenever you can

Try to stay at a healthy weight. If you need to lose weight following this advice, and making sure your fat and sugar intake are kept as low as possible, should result in a steady weight loss. Strict dieting is not recommended.

Don't smoke tips

The message is simple: DON'T SMOKE!

Smoking increases the risk of coronary heart disease by 50% and is the prime cause of premature deaths in the UK. Three elements make cigarettes and other tobacco products dangerous:

Nicotine

A powerful, fast acting and addictive drug that increases heart rate and blood pressure and constricts small blood vessels.

Carbon Monoxide

A poisonous gas found in high concentrations in cigarette smoke that causes problems with growth. It is particularly harmful during pregnancy.

Tar

70% of inhaled smoke is deposited on the lungs in the form of tar, causing a narrowing of the bronchioles, coughing, increased mucus and damage to the hairs that protect the lungs from dirt and infection.

Quitting smoking reduces the risk of coronary heart disease by half after 1 year and returns to that of a non-smoker after 4 years.

Blood pressure tips

The effects of high blood pressure are caused by blood being pumped round the body at a higher pressure, so the heart must work harder and

over time the heart muscle may become enlarged or stretched.

Many people don't realise they have high blood pressure as they feel no apparent symptoms. Smoking, being overweight, excessive alcohol and too much salt all play their part in high blood pressure.

There are ways of checking and combating high blood pressure:

- Have it checked by your GP every year.
- Excessive alcohol can cause high blood pressure, so drink sensibly.
- Avoid salt in your cooking whenever possible.

Need help or advice?

National Heart Research Fund, Concord House, Park Lane, Leeds LS3 1EQ. Telephone: (+44) 113 234 7474 Fax: (+44) 113 297 6208.

Nutrition and health

A useful guide

One way of looking at foods that better takes into consideration the characteristics of our modern world is as follows:

Foods rich in carbohydrates – broad, pasta, rice. yams, potatoes – should be seen as the largest single component of a meal or snack. These provide energy and some protein and a rich mixture of vitamins, minerals and fibre. Whole-grain cereal products are especially beneficial in this respect. It is a common misconception that carbohydrates, including sugars, are fattening. In fact, they contain only 4 kcal per gram, which is less than half the calories of fat.

Plenty of vegetables and fruit should also be included each day, either at meal times or as snacks. Not only do these provide additional vitamins and minerals, but they are also thought to be rich in elements which may help protect against certain chronic diseases such as coronary heart disease and cancer.

Diets should also contain foods rich in protein such as meat, or alternatives such as fish, poultry, eggs, bean-type vegetables, nuts or cheese. These foods are also rich in vitamins and minerals, and red meat is an important source of iron.

Energy-rich foods such as spreading and cooking fats. fried foods, cakes, pastries, biscuits and confectionery can be enjoyed in moderation. In reducing our total fat intake, we should reduce the amount of saturated fat we eat and ensure that we consume some mono-unsaturated fats (MUFA) and some polyunsaturated ones (PUFA) to provide the fatty acids essential for health. Saturated fats are found mainly in meats, dairy products and the hydrogenated vegetable oils used in baked products. PUFA occur in vegetables and fish oils, while some vegetable oils are rich in MUFA, Meat and dairy fat also contain some MUFA,

Water is vital to life and the intake of fluids has to be balanced over a shorter time – not more than a day – than the intake of nutrients. About half our water needs are provided by the foods we eat and the other half by drinks such as tap or bottled water, fruit juices, tea, coffee, soft drinks, and milk. Normally our total daily intake of water is around two litres.

It should be noted that this strategy contrasts somewhat with an approach common in many northern European countries. Here, consumers tend to base a meal around a protein-rich food such as meat or fish and accompany it with smaller amounts of carbohydrate-rich foods (such as bread, potatoes, rice or pasta) and vegetables.

ADDITIONAL RESOURCES

You might like to contact the following organisations for further information. Due to the increasing cost of postage, many organisations cannot respond to enquiries unless they receive a stamped, addressed envelope.

ASH – Action on Smoking and Health
102 Clifton Street
London, EC2A 4HW
Tel: 0171 739 5902
Fax: 0171 613 0531
E-mail:
action.smoking.health@dial.pipex.com
Web site: www.ash.org.uk
ASH is a campaigning organisation whose mission is to expose, control and publicise the damaging activities of the tobacco industry. They produce factsheets, postcards, posters and educational booklets.

ASH in Wales
374a Cowbridge Road East
Canton
Cardiff, CF5 1JJ
Tel: 01222 641101
Fax: 01222 641045
ASH in Wales campaigns to make the public more aware of the dangers of smoking, to prevent the death, disability and disease it causes and to make non-smoking a norm in society.

ASH – Northern Ireland
40-42 Eglantine Avenue
Belfast, BT9 6DX
Tel: 01232 663281
Fax: 01232 660081

ASH – Scotland
8 Frederick Street
Edinburgh, EH2 2HB
Tel: 0131 225 4725
Fax: 0131 220 6604
Ash Scotland is responsible for all ASH's work in Scotland and campaigns on all aspects of tobacco and health. One of ASH Scotland's main areas of interest is children and smoking.

British Heart Foundation (BHF)
14 Fitzhardinge Street
London, W1H 4DH
Tel: 0171 935 0185
Fax: 0171 486 5820
Web site: www.bhs.org.uk/
The aim of the British Heart Foundation is to play a leading role in the fight against heart disease and prevent death by ways including educating the public and health professionals about heart disease, its prevention and treatment. A more detailed leaflet, *The Heart – Technical Terms Explained*, is available free of charge from the BHF at the above address.

British Medical Association (BMA)
BMA House
Tavistock Square
London, WC1H 9JP
Tel: 0171 387 4499
Fax: 0171 383 6400
E-mail: bma.org.uk
Web site: www.bma.org.uk
The BMA lobbies and advises politicians on a number of smoking issues and launches regular media campaigns. Please note that the BMA does not have the resources to deal with individual student enquiries. However, they will respond to teachers' enquiries.

Health Education Authority
Trevelyan House
30 Great Peter Street
London, SW1P 2HW
Tel: 0171 222 5300
Fax: 0171 413 8900
Web site: www.hea.org.uk
The Health Education Authority is the national centre of excellence for health education research and expertise and, through its campaigns, publications and work with health professionals, encourages the public to adopt healthier lifestyles.

Health Education Board for Scotland (HEBS)
Woodburn House
Canaan Lane
Edinburgh, EH10 4SG
Tel: 0131 536 5500
Fax: 0131 536 5501
E-mail: hebsweb@hebs.scot.nhs.uk
Web site: www.hebs.scot.nhs.uk/lib
The Health Education Board for Scotland (HEBS) gives leadership to the health education effort in Scotland by playing its part in ensuring that people have adequate information about health and the factors which influence it

National Heart Research Fund
Concord House
Park Lane
Leeds, LS3 1EQ
Tel: 0113 234 7474
Fax: 0113 297 6208
Web site: www.heartresearch.org.uk/
Heart disease kills more people and damages more lives than any other disease in Britain today.
Heart Research is dedicated to raising money for vital research into the causes, treatment and prevention of heart disease so that people can enjoy fuller and healthier lives.

QUIT
Victory House
170 Tottenham Court Road
London, W1P 0HA
Tel: 0171 388 5775
Fax: 0171 388 5995
Helps smokers to try to give up. Co-operates with other charitable organisations.

INDEX

The Internet has been likened to shopping in a supermarket without aisles. The press of a button on a Web browser can bring up thousands of sites but working your way through them to find what you want can involve long and frustrating on-line searches. And unfortunately many sites contain inaccurate, misleading or heavily biased information. Our researchers have therefore undertaken an extensive analysis to bring you a selection of quality Web site addresses.

* * * * *

The British Heart Foundation (BHF)
www.bhf.org.uk
The British Heart Foundation aims to play a leading role in the fight against heart disease and provides research, support, education, training and equipment. Their web site contains information in support of these aims, notably a detailed listing and ordering facility for the many free publications produced by the Foundation, and Health Heart, a health promotion section dealing with physical activity, smoking, drinking, blood pressure and heart conditions.

HeartPoint
www.heartpoint.com
HeartPoint has been created by medical professionals to provide patients with a source of credible information about heart disease. US-based but useful.

The Grown Up Congenital Heart Patients Association (GUCH)
www.guch.demon.co.uk
Click on The Information Sheets link under the Resource Library heading for a wide range of information on congenital heart defects

Heart Information Network
http://heartinfo.org
HeartInfo is an independent, educational web site that provides a wide range of information and services to heart patients and others interested in learning about lowering risk factors for heart disease. Founded by a heart patient and a physician who is a renowned expert on heart disease, the site is dedicated to empowering individuals and fostering a dialogue between individuals and their physicians.

Merck & Co. Inc.
www.merck.com/disease/heart
Provides a large amount of reader-friendly information on heart disease.

The Coronary Prevention Group
www.healthnet.org.uk/facts
Their UK Virtual HealthNet web site helps you learn more about your health. An informative site with a wide range of interesting factsheets on heart disease related topics including the following: blood pressure, diet, smoking, exercise, stress, women and coronary heart disease, cardiac rehabilitation and cholesterol and your heart. Well worth a visit.

ACKNOWLEDGEMENTS

The publisher is grateful for permission to reproduce the following material.

While every care has been taken to trace and acknowledge copyright, the publisher tenders its apology for any accidental infringement or where copyright has proved untraceable. The publisher would be pleased to come to a suitable arrangement in any such case with the rightful owner.

Chapter One: What is Heart Disease?

Heart disease, © Reader's Digest Association Ltd, *Britain still tops European heart disease league*, © Telegraph Group Limited, London 1999, *Male deaths from heart disease*, © World Health Statistics, *Check your healthy heart I.Q.*, © US Department of Health and Human Services, National Institutes of Health, *Early warning test for smokers' hearts*, © Telegraph Group Limited, London 1999, *Study casts doubt on heart 'risk factors'*, © Telegraph Group Limited, London 1999, *Women and coronary heart disease*, © The Coronary Prevention Group, *Coronary heart disease*, © General Practice Research Database, Office for National Statistics (ONS), *Heart death rate more than twice European level*, © Telegraph Group Limited, London 1999, *Glasgow and Belfast top heart attack list*, © The Guardian, May 1999, *Risk factors*, © Women's Health Interactive, *Heart attack risk 'staring to vanish for the rich'*, © The Guardian, April 1999, *Worldwide trends*, © World Health Organisation (WHO), *About heart, stress and blood pressure*, © Boots the Chemists, *Heart terms explained*, © British Heart Foundation (BHF), *Coronary artery bypass graft*, © BUPA/Mosby International, *You and your heart*, © The Coronary Prevention Group, *Set your heart on eating well*, © Telegraph Group Limited, London 1999, *Coronary heart disease and stroke*, © Crown copyright material is reproduced with the permission of the Controller of Her Majesty's Stationery Office, *Facts about heart failure*, © US Department of Health and Human Services, National Institutes of Health.

Chapter Two: Preventing Heart Disease

How to prevent heart disease, © BUPA/Mosby International, *Exercise tips*, © National Heart Research Fund, *Healthy tips*, © Heartpoint, *Keep your heart healthy*, © BUPA 1996-99, *Public to operate heart machines*, © The Guardian, July 1999, *Exercise and the heart*, © The Coronary Prevention Group, *The price of a better – and longer – life*, © The Guardian, July 1999, *The 500 'who fail to survive waiting list for heart surgery'*, © The Daily Mail, June 1999, *Red wine no protection as French climb the heart disease league*, © The Guardian, May 1999, *NHS to target heart disease*, © The Guardian, October 1999, *Healthy lifestyles*, © National Heart Research Fund, *Nutrition and health*, © EUFIC.

Photographs and illustrations:

Pages 1, 2, 15, 17, 20, 29, 31, 34, 38, 40: Pumpkin House, pages 4, 6, 7, 11, 13, 19, 21, 25, 27, 32, 37, 39: Simon Kneebone.

Craig Donnellan
Cambridge
January, 2000

South East Essex College
of Arts & Technology